Dark Side of Heaven

Dark Side of Heaven

Lisa Palanca

with Lynn Harris

ISBN 978-1-7349642-2-6
ISBN 978-1-7349642-3-3
Published by Two Hands Publishing
Kalamazoo, Michigan

In loving memory of our mothers
Carla Palanca and Zenobia Marable

Prelude

The lake was calming. The bluff, with its beach grass looking more like a desperate middle aged man with hair plugs, sang a soft song as if to applaud the last bits of breathtaking sunset. If one listened closely, they could hear the hiss as the sun hit the water and watch in wonder as one brave flickering star soldiered forth. A constant in a crazy life. Waves with a steady rhythm on the sugar sand shore, marched in cadence to human breathing. It was this oneness often sought; harmonious and pure.

Rolling out of a sleeping house and sneaking to the bench that sat high above the water, Lisa allowed the sound of the waves to stroke her like a nurturing mother. Sometimes the lake was roiled up and wanton. Large, building white caps seemed in competition for the shore, the winner wave sneaking through like a snake while the others crashed and died to the side. Wind whipped the beach so hard at times sand pummeled her skin like an abrasive. She was that wild wind, unharnessed and angry. Tonight, she was happy to find a soothing limpid flatness and the repetitive soft lap of waves on the shore. Closing her eyes, she let the gentle waves speak to her.

People spoke of a childhood in this town as idyllic. Nestled between dunes and open beach, it had been an escape destination for many living in larger cities, for at least 100 years. The history of the land mentioned that its beauty was home to the Chippewa and Pottawattamie Indian tribes. They trapped beaver and mink to trade with the French in the Upper Peninsula. These hides afforded the Native Americans a competitive price. The French milliners could not get enough of the fur. They would use them to make high stove top hats that were worn by men of high stature in Europe.

It was on one of these fur trading excursions that entrepreneurs began to notice the richness of the lush forests. Lucrative, at first, it was soon "discovered" by lumber tycoons, grappling at the chance to buy more and more acreage to keep up with the burgeoning building boom.

Situated just about 125 miles from Chicago, Heaven could be reached by a steamer ship charging 25 cents for a one way crossing. The ship lifted anchor twice a day to bring people away from the city to the rolling farmland, lightly populated beaches, and quiet serenity of an unhurried pace.

Cool breezes off the lakeshore provided comfort to the sizzling concrete. Chicago businessmen took the opportunity to send their entire families to the shore in Southwest Michigan for the summer months. It allowed them to focus on their businesses without distraction. On Fridays, fathers and husbands joined together to caravan around the base of Lake Michigan north to Heaven for a reunion with their families. Many of the resorts and cottages were being built featuring rambling porches and comfortable lounge chairs. Dance halls and restaurants became abundant, and locals in the small town were only too happy to have the cash. Many of the men, including gangster Al Capone, would say they had "classed up" the itty bitty town.

The Great Migration of African Americans caused the Michigan population to surge. As early as the 1900's small mixed race communities of white and black ancestry settled in Southwestern Michigan. Unlike the draw of industry to the east in Detroit, these towns boasted black and white family farms coexisting side by side. Settling on cheap farm land, the immigrants from Europe and the influx of freed blacks from the South set up an almost harmonious living arrangement.

It had almost lasted. But human beings, as they are, often want more. Contentment is an elusive dream.

In this town called Heaven, lumber tycoons and other entrepreneurs wanted to change the slow and easy way of life by making capital. Money was the name of their game. They rapidly built a collection of small industrial factories. By the 1960's, these factories had lured many newcomers to earn a reasonable wage. Working side by side, the race and ethnicity factors had not really been an issue. Folks kept to their own kind. But the lines of division were still felt.

When Lisa Palma and Lynn Parris were ready for kindergarten at the public school, a rumbling of unrest could be felt. On the national stage, civil rights inequity was disrupting the American Dream. The rags to riches stories could be written mainly for white European immigrants or those coming into the United States willingly. The legacy of the freed slave presented a much more difficult route to success.

The reality of Jim Crow Laws being a southern thing was being disproved over and over again in the north. It became increasingly clear that there was a demarcation of whom would find success or live with mediocrity. The 1960's were becoming a time of new realizations of bias in both religion and race relations. The historical good 'ole boy networks had not been altered by an awakening of empathy. Stairways to success were often based upon who you knew and not what. The small community was assumed to be a multi-racial group of people living in harmony but entitlement lines were blurring. A set of unsaid and unwritten rules had settled over Michigan. In Heaven, the relationships between races hadn't changed much. As long as everyone kept in step, a peaceful life could go on. Residents knew their place. Ultimately the order from best to least was: white man, white married women, white single women, black men with a job, black married women, and black single women.

A divide was being formed with an invisible line in the 1960's. After decades of building up the American black men and women, it was as if the nation was dragging its feet on how much more they would collectively allow. Would there be equality between them?

Within Heaven's city limits, a four block square was cleared where small, federally funded HUD houses were built near the public schools. Adjacent to the park and factories, people called the area the Zone. It was as if the black people in town had heard the call to circle their wagons, because the Zone housed most of the African American families in the entire town.

As if slapped in the face, the nation began to take notice.

Black citizens, who were used to "taking it" began to boil over with protests. The symbiotic dynamic that made this small town special was sagging under the pressure.

It seemed unfathomable that a little black girl and a little white girl would begin to form an unbreakable bond that lasted for more than 50 years.

Lisa

The sun would be blazing if she didn't get up now, Lisa thought. as she pulled herself out of bed. Her sturdy 10 year old frame and short stature made it easy to scramble down from the top bunk without waking her little sister. They had shared this bedroom since Jane was born. Lisa had fallen instantly in love with the new baby. But now, at 5, her sister would most likely want to tag along and that would be counterproductive to the cause. The focus this morning was to make enough money to surprise Jane and treat her to ice cream.

She hastily pulled on a pair stretchy red shorts with a matching tank top. Her mother loved to buy "outfits". Lisa decided to pass on pawing through her underwear drawer for fresh panties. She skipped deodorant. There would certainly be some aroma from her armpits after spending a whole morning in the hot sun. She didn't like this idea of growing up if it meant stinking. A quick dip at Deerlick Beach to freshen up on her way back home would solve this problem. The bathroom mirror wasn't sending off too many alarms in her appearance, just suggesting a quick comb through her tousled hair. Don't worry about what you are wearing, her inner voice told her, just put your flip flops on and go.

It was the pure love of blueberries that could propel her body out of bed. Normally, rise and shine might not be for a couple more hours. But mid-July was the beginning of the harvest, and this little town in the mitten of Michigan was beginning to boast its claim as the "Blueberry Capital of the World." Her brother Billy and his friend Pat had planned a day of money making by picking several gallons themselves, and she had asked to tag along. Billy was only a year older than her. She was obviously an "Oops" child (as her mom told the other mothers on the block) who shared her firsts with her brother's firsts. Ready or not, Lisa gave up her bottle, diapers, and pacifier when he did. Her mother was just too tired to deal with extra childcare since she had three babies under 5 years old at the time. Billy seemed to resent her for tagging along and did his best to push her away.

Yesterday, she came upon Pat and Billy lounging around in the shade of the backyard Maple tree. Pat always had a protective sweet spot for her. He was a chunky blond of German descent and smiled as she sat down next to him.

"We're heading out early to Champ's Blueberries to pick tomorrow. You want to come with?" He said to Lisa in a lazy way.

"Can I really?" She had asked knowing it was a must to secure her spot before her brother used his veto power.

"The more the merrier," Pat said looking over at Billy. "Right Billy?"

"As long as you can keep up." He'd said rolling his eyes at Pat. "We aren't going to wait for her."

Lisa had been giddy with excitement thinking about the amount of berries needed in order to make enough money to buy ice cream. A time estimate of an hour probably, she thought.

Mother started giving instructions as she walked out the door.

"You need to stay together."

That was it. In this small town, everyone watched what everyone else's kids were doing. If they got out of line, her mother would certainly know about it before they even got home.

Fueled with Shredded Wheat cereal and sugar, they took to their bicycles. Billy was leading the charge on his stingray. Pat was close behind; his bike almost identical to Billy's except for the color. Billy's was blue and Pat's was red. Lisa felt that the practice of handing things down was never quite fair. Her bicycle was a birthday present to her sister Marcy, who barely rode it, was given to Billy who banged it up like it was his job, and now belonged to Lisa. It was rusty and dented and the kickstand was missing. The chain liked to fall off on hills. But she wasn't even bothered about these things today, as her mission was to keep up with the boys until they reached the U Pick Lot at Champ's. It was only about a mile from their home but the two steep hills between the locations meant Lisa had to try to get fast momentum on the down slope so that she wouldn't be tasked with the hard pedal back up and the possibility of losing her chain. Luckily for her, the chain was in good spirits that day. As they slowed to pull into the lot, she was covered with sweat and her heart was beating so hard she could feel it in her ears.

Parking their bikes in the bike rack they walked to the truck to get their gallon pails. Keeping up with the boys was making Lisa walk/jog to stay with them. Technically, they would get to bring home a little less than a half of the first gallon they picked. Payment was $1.00 a bucket and pickers could keep half a gallon to take home. The rest of the berries went to the farm's wholesale store.

Arriving at the first row of blueberry bushes, Lisa's goal was to pick at least 3 buckets. After 30 minutes her enthusiasm was waning. She looked inside. The bottom of the gallon bucket barely had an inch of berries. She began to make alternative plans. Maybe she would just pick 2 gallons, she thought. Jane might have to have a small cone at the Dairy Store. It was better than nothing.

Imagining her Fudge Ripple ice cream cone kept her mind off of physical discomfort and, as she picked the first bucket carefully, she filled up on a berry breakfast, when no one was looking. This was what summer felt like. She breathed in the scent of blueberries with just enough dew on their leaves. Juicy navy blue berry goodness would go into muffins, pies, crisps, coffeecakes, or just plain bowls. Mom would put a bowl of them in the fridge for snacking.

The sun was fully up now. In her haste to get ready, Lisa realized how woefully unprepared she was for the sun, bugs, and sweat of the blueberry patch. She was swatting mosquitoes the size of quarters, each one extracting an ounce of blood. Her skin was puffing up in every area. Kicking herself for chuckling when Pat had tried to hide his neck from the sun with a bandana she heard him say:

"You're gonna burn to a crisp today."

She had thought the precaution to prevent sunburn was silly for her and her family. Pat wasn't lucky like she was, with her Italian olive skin. He burned quickly in the sun often the first signs being the pink tinges on his ears and nose. She had wondered what it even felt like to have a sunburn. Tans were all the rage, she knew. Some people really worked on them. There was a Coppertone advertisement she especially loved of a dog pulling down the bathing suit bottoms of a very tan girl to reveal the whiteness underneath. She could do that at home in front of the mirror, but usually her tan was pretty even and she knew others were envious. It was not something she tried to do on purpose. Her dark glossy hair and very brownish black eyes seemed to naturally go with a mocha color for her skin. Her grandpa had called it Cappuccino Amore or something.

But looking over at Pat, in the adjacent row across the path, she realized he was cool as a cucumber with his bandana up on his neck and a baseball cap with its long brim shielding the bright scorch of the sun. He also had worn a long sleeve shirt and old tennis shoes. How dumb, she felt, looking at her berry stained feet in flip flops. Her left sandal stretched and dangerously close to breaking and causing the veritable "flat tire". She would have to throw it away if that happened. That would make the barefoot bike ride home more miserable.

Questioning her motivation being ice cream, she looked at her first gallon bucket. There had been no progress getting to the fill line in the last 10 minutes. She would never make her goal! Billy and Pat had filled two buckets already and were well onto their third. A drink of water was needed.

She made it over to the water tank on the truck, moving

the bucket she had tied over her shoulder aside, to grab the top paper cup from the tube.

The supervisor of the lot, one of the older Champ boys, looked at her and said:

"Hey! You're late!" He called down from high up the back gate of the pickup. "The Mexican pickers just left for the outer field. You'll have to walk out there, I can't take you."

For a second, drinking her water, Lisa didn't realize he was talking to her.

"Hey! You're a Hernandez, aren't you?" He jumped down and shouted right in her face.

She looked around. Was this guy talking to her? Didn't he know who she was? Heck, she thought everyone in town knew her family.

"I'm a Palma," She said saucily. How dare this dude think she was a Mexican!

"Oh, my gosh! I am so sorry." He laughed. "You have a pretty dark tan there."

Lisa let silence fall over the conversation. It was so still they could hear the trucks out on Blue Star Highway.

"Yeah. I think I am done picking now." She began to remove her bucket from her shoulder even though it was just half full.

"You aren't leaving because of what I said, are ya?" He queried.

"Not really. Maybe. Of Course! I'm just going to tell my dad what you called me. I don't think he will be happy."

"No. Don't tell your dad, please! What can I do to make this right?" The Champ kid was squirming.

She whispered "Can I get $3.00 for this?"

Lisa learned early the pull her father had in town. No one wanted to cross him as he was a very proud Italian with a stereotypical Italian temper.

"Well, you haven't even filled your second basket!" He chortled.

"And you called me a Mexican," she said indignantly with her hand out, waiting. "My dad, well, I am pretty sure he would say you were cutting me down."

"Um. No." The kid was wrestling in his mind, she could tell, the idea of her dad coming here versus the loss of a couple dollars of profit. "So, I am sorry about that. Sure, I will give you $3.00." He said sheepishly. "Go ahead and use that box for your berries to take home too."

He gave her a look like he had just tasted something sour. It wasn't like she intentionally wanted him to dislike her. The point was, this berry business sucked. It was hard. She wanted to be done. This was a way out and she capitalized on the whole misunderstanding. Manipulation was a learned skill, and she was becoming a master at it.

The box he pointed to was much bigger than her take should have been. She filled it to the brim, beginning to feel a little churn in her gut. What was the deal with this Mexican thing? It made her feel bad. But yet, she knew you didn't get ahead unless you took charge. She would probably brag about it later to her friends. They would nod and applaud. Praise would be bestowed on her for knowing how to handle a teenager at her age. Just keeping my image, she thought.

Billy and Pat were way far out in the middle of the U Pick lot. She turned to the Champ kid, who was wishing she would just go away.

"Hey. Tell my brother I left," she said.

Steadying her bike, she balanced the box on the handle bars. Things were bothering her. It felt like when she put up three posters on her wall and one had been a little uneven. It unsettled her and made her feel off center. Not cool.

The whole blueberry experience would have been better if she had never gone. With each pedal she tried to think of any Mexicans she might know. There were none. She had seen groups around town and at church. There were always more families in the summers and fall but she didn't remember them going to school at St. Leonard's or being around during the winter. Grandma showed her the little houses on farms around the county. But grandma called them migrant worker housing, not Mexican housing. Once, Lisa watched a family have a picnic near the beach. They had moved well down where the rocks made swimming hazardous. The ladies laid out food, filling her with wonder. Sandwiches were made on flat bread thinner than pancakes. The family laughed and cavorted around the sand speaking strange words faster than the speed of light. When they saw her watching, they quieted down. The joy left their eyes and was replaced by wariness. Actually, their strangeness scared her a little bit.

Shaking her head to erase these deep, heavy thoughts there was a bright side. She had blueberries! She would share them with her family and her friend Sadie. But the idea of going for ice cream on this berry money seemed wrong. Suddenly, she didn't feel so good. No ice cream trip today.

She needed to talk this out with her best friend. She threw her bike down on the front lawn and ran into the house. She left the box open and scooped a bunch of berries into a bowl. She called Sadie and told her to meet her at their spot on the lake bank.

It was a beautiful thing to walk past one house on their small street and see Lake Michigan. It was the only lake she had known in her short life, and she marveled at how many "tourists" would walk down to the bench at the end of the street each evening and watch the sunset. Yes, it was pretty and all but it happened every day no matter where you lived.

Summer tourists made her ornery. They ambled down her neighborhood street and tramped over people's lawns to take pictures. There was a great view of the bright red lighthouse at the end of the south pier and these summer visitors were often oblivious to swarms of gnats, mosquitoes, and black flies. They would do anything to get a shot.

This summer was shaping up to be another stinker with the alewife fish die off. Alewives were small silver fish that died off by the hundreds every six to ten years. Their bodies floated on the water and when it reached the shore the sun glinted off the silver fish in a way that was almost blinding. If the wind was just right, the putrid stench of their rotting bodies would hang, as if suspended in the air. There would be no escaping the thick aroma and there likely would be fewer summer people standing on the bank. Swimming was not for the faint of heart during this time either. The waves would pull hundreds of fish out to sea and the next roller would deliver a hundred more to the beach. Dead or dying surfers on their last ride. City workers raked them up into piles and burned them at night: the black pyres delivering smoke that was tastable. Few homes had air conditioning, still the windows remained closed, the toss up of sleep loss due to stink winning over night cooled air.

Thankfully, conditions weren't quite that bad yet. She and Sadie picked their bowl of blueberries up and hopped over the lake bank digging into the sand with bare heels to control their pace down the soft, squishy ridge to the beach.

Lisa asked Sadie: "Do I look like a Mexican to you?"

"A Mexican?" Sadie asked. "Of course not. You look like an Italian."

The way she said *Italian* made Lisa feel better. Sadie's family was so much whiter than she was. Her green eyes and blonde hair were testament to that. Sadie always had clothes from stores in big towns like Kalamazoo and St. Joe. Her mom took her a couple times a year on clothes runs to places like Jacobson's and Rime's Department stores. Often gone all day, they would come back around dinner time having spent the day and "doing lunch." Lisa would watch from her front window as bag after bag of clothes, packed in boxes and covered with tissue paper, were dug out of the Lincoln Continental that Sadie's mother drove. Mere minutes passed before the phone rang and Sadie would call Lisa to come and see what her new haul contained.

Perhaps there should be a twinge of jealousy, but there wasn't. It was just one of those accepted things. Sadie got clothes from nice, expensive stores and Lisa got clothes from the catalog and picked them up at the catalog store. Lisa didn't feel bad about it. Sure, it would be nice to be the first off-the-rack buyer of clothes, but she got the next best thing—Sadie's hand-me-downs!

They were the inevitable bonuses for Lisa and her sister Jane. Each time after shopping, Sadie would need closet space to hang her new dresses and jumpers and blouses and sweaters.

"We cleaned the closets," Sadie would sing into the phone. "Come on over and pick out what you would like."

This was a bonanza day! Since Lisa was a little smaller in stature than Sadie, she was able to take most of the cast-offs home to wear. She loved those days. One wool jumper that Sadie never wore was worn by Lisa, her sister, and two girls from an entirely different family! Often the clothes were of much better quality than Sears or Montgomery Ward. The colors were up-to-date and classic. No paisleys or fishnets allowed.

The dresses became Sunday best dresses for Lisa and her sister Jane. Palma's wore uniforms to school at St. Leonard's. Lisa's old play clothes would be passed down. There wasn't a kid in the Palma house that cared if their clothes were new or not. The twins often fought to not have to wear matching clothes. Her older sister, Marcy, had a job and bought her own clothes. Sometimes being the oldest, she was able to charge her things at the Heaven department store to the Palma account. The boys often wore sports jerseys or tee shirts that came in packs of three.

Once the dust had settled and Sadie's clothes had been meted out, Lisa would balance a coffee cake plate in her hands and walk it down to Sadie's house. Carla Palma was good at paying gratitude with baked goods. Lisa wondered what Sadie's family did with the baked coffee cake. It was pretty rustic baking compared to Mrs. Ryan's chocolate cake with marshmallow frosting. The Ryan family were rail thin. Sadie was a super picky eater. But whenever Lisa walked through the door, Mrs. Ryan would not even have to ask, she would take down one of her beautiful cake plates, edged in gold and displaying perfect birds of exotic places. Placing a wedge of cake on a plate, she'd ask Lisa to be the taste tester.

Lisa loved Mrs. Ryan so much. She treated her as if she *saw* her. If there wasn't cake, there were chocolate eclairs and long johns (along with a few loaves of freshly baked bread) that Mr. Ryan would pick up every few days from the little bakery downtown. Lisa didn't know anyone else who bought or ate bakery bread all the time. Wonder Bread was the bread of choice in their house. Spongy, white goodness smeared with Jif peanut butter. Bakery bread turned tough and hard only days after purchase, or at least it did at her house. But then, rich people had different tastes.

Even the smells inside their houses were different. Sadie's house smelled like butter and sugar and beef cooking slowly covered with herbs. Lisa's mother cooked great dinners but they weren't fancy. Lisa knew she should feel lucky to have meat, potatoes, a salad, and two vegetables most every day. Yet, sometimes, when she walked into her house, the smell of grease from the hamburger patties covered with mushroom soup would make her long for Mrs. Ryan's homemade vegetable soup.

So many wonderful dishes Mrs. Ryan would make! They were a family who didn't sit down at a table to eat. They ate in the den or in their rooms sometimes. Sadie's favorite meal was Kraft cheese singles. She would eat them, broken in fourths, with saltine crackers. Legs crossed Indian-style on her bed as Lisa lay on the floor and talked to her, Sadie would never go in for the main course of the day, and her mother didn't force her to eat brussel sprouts or lima beans like at the Palma's. Sadie had her own television. It was a small black and white portable with its own antennae. It got all the good channels and Lisa was surprised that there were more networks than CBS one night when she slept over.

Sadie went to public school. It surprised Lisa that she did. Even Lisa's Catholic school, St. Leonard's, was better than the scary kids that came from farms or Parade Avenue. There were pockets of groups of friends based on neighborhoods. On Apache Court, there were three families that went to St. Leonard's and three families that went to public school. It was a good balance and probably kept everyone friendly as there was no competition for prizes or awards. Time would tell when they got into the one common high school. As older siblings headed there it really didn't seem so bad. Actually, it was kind of exciting to have all Heaven's kids finally together.

Lisa had public school friends but they were mostly Sadie's friends. The Ryan family had been well established in the community for at least a century. Sadie's father took over his father's business. It did very well. It was called the "Book and Craftt Shop" and it was also the bus station. The store sold magazines, tourist souvenirs, and books. Ryan's had a baby grand piano in their sunken living room that Sadie played in an accomplished way. When she practiced Lisa sat beside her and turned pages of the music book at her nod.

Sadie's family loved to entertain. Sometimes they took Lisa along to Saugatuck to spend the day with Sadie at the pool of a country club their friends owned. The girls swam the entire day, and when they were hungry they ordered hamburgers and fries from the pool waitress. Sadie signed her dad's name on the bill.

With bloodshot eyes from chlorinated pool water the girls reluctantly followed the instruction to take showers after swimming. Picking up the baby shampoo and little soaps, they showered in the clubhouse women's locker room. The vanity area was supplied with perfume samples, deodorants, lotions, and small canisters of hairspray. Around 5:00 PM, when they met the parents and their friends, they were walking clouds of fragrance. The adults laughed and said things about the boudoir.

With so many menu options, they were told to order whatever they wanted from the menu. But it wouldn't matter what they had on the menu because Lisa always ordered fried shrimp and Sadie- a filet mignon. Clicking together "Kiddie Cocktails" they kept themselves busy until the adults finished and it was time to leave. Arriving home late, Artie sleepily opened the door and thanked Mr. Ryan for seeing Lisa home. He took her hand, tucked her in, and went up to his bed to sleep. She made him hold her sometimes extra-long.

Big world things often made Lisa more afraid than she needed to be. Sometimes she awoke with a start, shaking in a cold sweat. Her recurring fear was of looking out the window to see a face. When they had seen the documentary on Amelia Earhart being lost in the Pacific Ocean, Lisa reasoned that she might have been lost over the Lake Michigan. Maybe she had clawed her way up the lake bank and was frantically trying to signal that she was alive by looking through windows in the dark of night. Storms, tornado warnings, blizzards, and what was happening in Vietnam were traumatizing to her. Several times the neighborhood kids watched the Coast Guard retrieve wreckage from boats in the choppy seas of the lake, usually after a storm. She and Sadie played lookout for them, setting chairs on the lake bluff where Sadie's lawn ended. Booming thunder echoed as storms approached from miles away. Darkening skies caught fishermen and pleasure boaters racing at top speed to get back to the channel and to safety. The girls watched for stragglers and were quite well known down at the station for putting out alerts for boats still out on the lake.

Sister Rosina, the first grade teacher, had said that God told the people on earth they would not know the day or hour He would come back. So, each day, almost every hour, Lisa said out loud, "Today the world will end." as if to give insurance for another day to not worry about the Second Coming. Knowing she was safe, in a world that was upside down was the daily, number one thing on her to do list.

Lynn

Lynn was not born in Michigan. Her early memories were of sirens and horns honking. Life on this side of Lake Michigan was filled with urban pleasures. Deep Dish Chicago pizza, rides on the el train, up to date releases of music albums, and ice cream trucks stationed on city block corners.

She came into the world in a Chicago hospital down the street from her home. This city had a pulse that never slowed and this was ever etched into her little brain. The flashing lights of police strobes walked over her bedroom walls as she lay in her crib. She marveled at the way the lights danced when there was more than one police car outside.

Lynn Parris grew up insulated in the love of family. Not a day went by without her seeing an auntie or playing with a cousin. The days when she learned to walk were celebrated by her mother and her brother. She babbled happily as she and her brother Lamar played outside. However cold or hot, the two were inseparable outdoors. It was a time she grew up to cherish.

Lamar had been looking out for Lynn her whole life, she thought. He was strong and a little lighter shade of skin. His green eyes got respect as he ventured out on the streets of Chicago. In fact, there was very little in common when it came to their looks. Lynn's dark complexion made vibrant clothes pop right on her skin, her mother said. Often mama would outfit her little girl in eye-catching clothes that she bought on sale at Marshall Field's on good days, and Kmart when the funds were low. Lynn captivated people with her wide happy smiles and fun filled demeanor. She had no reason to be sad. She was fed and loved and looked after.

Although the playgrounds situated within walking distance from their apartment were strictly off limits, they made a game of walking to the fenced in park a few blocks away. Mama had specifically said that a whooping with a belt would be a "given" if they were to wander into any of the closer parks. They were clearinghouses for young thugs and drug dealers. Zenobia feared the lure of gangs would ultimately take Lamar over someday and she would do her damnedest to prevent it from happening.

Mama worked a lot in those days. Her job at Supreme Liberty Life Insurance Company was the main source of income, and as breadwinner for the family, she was not going to have her four children placed in unsafe areas. But she had to travel many blocks to the building on South Park Street. She had searched through church acquaintances and family members until she found a cousin who would take care of Eva and Patsy. The two young girls were just toddlers, and since Cousin Rachele lived in the same building, she came up to Zenobia's early every morning to watch the babies at home for a few dollars a week.

Lamar and Lynn went along with Zenobia every day. She wanted Lamar far away from the local streets.

Mama took them to a different sitter on the Yellow Line bus. The sitter's name was Sherell who was a friend of mama's best friend Dorothy, and lived up near the Cabrini Green area. The route was a long, time consuming trek that woke the family a full hour and a half before punching in for work at 9:00. Rousting the children out of bed at 7:00, preparing a warm bowl of oatmeal in the winter or cereal in the summer, making sure they were clothed, shoed, and had used the restroom took up most of the morning routine.

Lynn loved swinging her legs on the bench at the bus stop. They never waited more than a few minutes. One morning, shortly after the new benches were installed, Lynn ran to get there first. She found a man asleep with a newspaper over his face and a cardboard box for a blanket. She lifted the newspaper ever so slowly, when a hand came out of nowhere and slapped her tiny fingers.

"Cover him up now!" Her mother growled.

"But Mama," Lynn whispered, "It's Uncle James!"

"I said cover him!" Zenobia spat.

Lynn did as she was told. She knew that James and her mama were not on very good terms. He was given a place to sleep in the apartment many times because he was Daddy's brother. James lived a hard life and could not ever seem to land on his feet. Lynn remembered her daddy asking his wife if his brother could stay a while. He had the habit of bringing in strays and Mama had a big heart. But, when she had to put her foot down, everyone knew that was the final word.

So, Lynn quickly covered up the unconscious face, as her

mother's tone was dangerous. Next, Mama had marched the children a full block over to catch the bus at a different stop. She didn't want James to wake up and recognize her today. She simply did not have the time for charity.

Mama was organized, Lynn thought, as she reflected on her life in Chicago. She had to be. They would take the bus to Sherell's house. She'd been a good friend and babysat the children at all times. Mama would get them situated on the sofa with their blankets, as Sherell was only just getting up and around. Giving a hasty goodbye and quick kiss, Zenobia would thank Sherell for taking care of her babies and run out to catch the Red Line bus that would transport her to work.

Sherell had a niece, Wanda, who came at 8:15AM to escort Lamar to school. His school was located only a few streets away. It was a public school but Zenobia used Sherell's address to get Lamar a spot there. After school, Wanda picked up Lamar and they would ride the city bus back to Zenobia's. Wanda often started the dinner for the family, and accepted $10 per week. It really took a network of family and good friends to take care of her children as she worked. But having three babysitters made things feel out of hand sometimes.

It was a well-orchestrated dance. Anything could throw off the rhythm. A cough, a stomach ache, or a lost shoe were dreaded obstacles some mornings. It was the one fear that made Zenobia want to be closer to her parents. She was beginning to get beaten down by the stress.

The view from the bus window often reminded Zenobia of the structure of an Oreo cookie – hard chocolate outside flanking a creamy smooth white center. For each day, she left a black neighborhood, went through a white neighborhood, and got off at another black neighborhood. She wished she could live closer to her job, but as this area was emerging, it still had not been overhauled by urban renewal. Signs of poverty and criminal activity were all around. It seemed as if the African American community was angry. She watched storefront after storefront close up in her part of the city. Grocery stores were caged to keep theft and crimes at a minimum. The local Jewel grocery began to employ more black workers, and it was proving to cause less anguish when unemployed mothers produced welfare coupon booklets at the checkout counters.

The times were changing. The buildings seemed to pulse with the energy of unfulfilled dreams. New mothers were cranking out babies without the help of a father figure. Zenobia was thankful that her children had solid role models in her own parents, who lived on a farm in Michigan. The quaintness of their little town was enticing, but its lack of possible employment soured her on moving there. Chicago could take her children to other countries for free with a visit to the Museum of Science and Industry or the Field Museum. Chicago offered cultural experiences in the theaters and the Art Institute. There were many free programs for kids. They leaned mostly on her church for guidance and community.

Zenobia was happy with her small, two-bedroom apartment for now. The rent was continuing to go up each year and she was just scraping by like everyone else. Soon, even this place would surpass her budget.

Garbage pickup was spotty, if they came at all. There were several times where Zenobia would take a brown shopping bag of garbage from the apartment and drop it at a random set of metal cans down an alley on her way to the bus. One day, she caught Lynn happily munching on a cracker filled with ants. Wiping the filth off her face, she told her never to go into the brown bags for any reason. Lynn cried loudly for her cracker. It was times like these that weighed on her mind. These things along with passing groups huddled secretly in the stairway of her apartment house, and the noise of other families arguing or love making through the paper thin walls, which made Zenobia wonder if she was doing right by her children.

She could defend herself only by saying that her children were fed and loved. She was doing better than most. Education was the key to her children's success and she was seeing to it that Lamar and Lynn would attend a city-honored public school.

The Supreme Liberty Life Insurance Building was located on the fringe of a predominantly white area. Zenobia Parris was so proud to work at a job that held so much significance for her as a black woman. It was the first African American life insurance company in the United States. Her boss, Frank Gillespie, Jr., made it a personal point of pride for his employees.

With his suspenders busting through his jacket, he shared his story about white owned life insurance companies denying black customers to own life insurance. When Frank's father began the company, in the 1920's, many of its white competitors thought it was a silly venture. They didn't believe that any black employee would want to put money into a fund to take care of their family, should they pass early. Frank Gillespie, Sr., had gambled on his friends and acquaintances' sense of family to invest a portion of their weekly take-home pay to an account with his company. It became the main life insurance company for the Chicago area black population and had been for decades. "The sweet deal of a lifetime" was Gillespie's motto.

Zenobia mulled things over as she looked out the window on the long bus rides home. She counted the ladies who had begun to gather on the corners to make a buck. Some she knew by name. There was an edge of danger when the night fell in the city. There was nothing safe about them. Although this area drew many during "the Great Migration" from the South, it had proved to be a place of great degradation to those who settled here. City parks and common areas were littered with bodies of the hopeless. People in search of a fast job with high pay were often met with disappointment. The promise of jobs was evaporating as crowds of southern blacks alit from the crowded Grand Central Station to a world that was cold, dark, and often separate. Many came without any urban living experience and were easily lured into crime, drugs, and gangs. No matter how hard they tried, bad luck was always around the corner.

That's how it had gone for her husband. Freddie had come up through Mississippi as a teen and his aunties were in charge of his spiritual journey. The Greater Union Baptist Church was famous for their ministry with African American parishioners. When Zenobia met Freddie 8 years ago, she had told her mother she wanted to marry him. Her mother had laughed and said to wait until he found a good, decent job. Freddie went to the Iron

Works in Gary to work and just like that, the pair was married.

It didn't take long for Freddie to lose his job as the added pressure of a baby and an unemployed wife were more than he could stand. The writing was on the wall the first time Zenobia found Freddie passed out on the fire escape. He had not even felt the bluster of the 20 degree wind, and when Zenobia took him inside, he slammed her hard against the wall.

"Woman, don't move me when I am sleeping!" He cried, delivering a powerful whack across her mouth.

Zenobia fled to her parents' house in Michigan. They helped her process divorce papers. She wanted to stay but life in that small town had been difficult. She felt like a failure. Knowing that another baby was on the way, she decided to take her small brood back into the city where there was more opportunity to find a decent job.

Mama is always asking God to help Lamar, Lynn mused. He was starting first grade that year. Lamar had been taught the value of living a good, respectable life. It wouldn't be easy to keep him away from the neighborhood gangs every minute. The little boys were often prey and enticed into making drug deliveries or collecting lottery cash. These boys could be bought for the promise of candy or toys. For many, this early indoctrination into easy money left them stuck with no way out.

Zenobia prayed each day from her seat on the bus, "Lord, Jesus, please keep my babies safe."

Focused on her job with her head down, she worked a nine hour shift. The job was interesting and she was good at it. Since working for two years she had been promoted twice.. Zenobia worked under Cornelius Watt, a fine man, who gave her stacks of work to process and return to him. He patted her head while he took the credit for her excellent skills. She never complained that he left things to her most of the time while he stepped out to lunch or the barber shop. Having the validation that she was doing things well was enough. It made her proud.

Tonight, the bus stopped a short half block from Sherell's. Zenobia hoisted herself from the bus seat and sighed. Time for the second shift, she thought. It was a familiar feeling. Thirty years old was right around the corner. Why was she so tired of this never ending cycle? There were still some hours of work for her as she made dinner, washed the kids up, told the bedtime stories, and said prayers. Longing for 8:30 PM, when she could pour herself a small drink of cream sherry and listen to some blues from the radio, she wondered if this battle to be the provider would ever get easier. Her constant anxiety was the thought that she might be responsible for putting her children in harm's way. Certainly, they were surrounded by enough family and friends, but she could not orchestrate the minute by minute details. It worried her.

Would she ever find another partner? Her friends had paraded a slew of men by her, but they just could not pass her scrutiny.

She had to be a working mother right now. She was deeply envious as she watched television shows where mothers stayed at home and took care of the kids. She just did not have that luxury. Most women she knew worked. At least her job was not as a domestic servant in a white household.

Hanging firmly to the handrail, she came off the bus and walked up to Sherell's door, looking this way and that for unseemly characters.

"Sherell, it's Zenobia." She shouted into the locked grate over the open screen door. Today had been a warm one.

"Hey Zenobia," Sherell said. "Got time for a cup of tea?"

Zenobia smiled. Sherell said this every day but there was no tea involved. It was either Kool-Aid, water, or if she was lucky, a taste of something stronger. Today, though, Sherell made some lemonade.

"I can't stay today Sherell," she said. "Rain check?"

"Okay. Well, here comes your princess." Lynn came to the door looking radiant in the paper crown Sherell made for her.

It made Zenobia smile. But as she looked her over, she noticed Lynn was not in the clothes she came in with this morning.

"Um, Sherell?" Zenobia said.

"Oh my goodness, her clothes!" She laughed. "They opened the hydrants today and I let the babies go in the puddle once it was off. Damn near blew away some of the older boys. There was a regular congregation of them. Don't you worry, I will never let the girls go anywhere without me."

Lynn's smile was ear to ear as she told her mother about the fun time they'd had in the water. Her mother was quick to point out that she was never to be out of Sherell's sight when she was outdoors. It sucked all the light out of Lynn's day. Why did Mama always do this? If she had her way, Lynn and her brother would never get out and play. Everything was frightening and wrong. She wished her mother could quit worrying about work and money and food and all the things that made her seem tired.

But she knew that Mama had to worry enough for two parents. The divorce had been almost a year ago and although mama still did all the things she used to, she also had the burden of being a babysitter and watch out for her children.

Lynn never saw her daddy. Her main protector now was her older brother, Lamar. Why, just yesterday, Lynn screamed over the night crawler in the gutter, as if it was an Anaconda. She was the damsel in distress with Lamar as her knight in shining armor. He ran into the house and brought out the gallon jug of Clorox bleach. They stood side by side watching it shrivel up. Lynn looked at him with genuine love. She never would have been able to think so quickly on her feet. But she wasn't the only one watching. Lamar was being eyed by the Black Disciples. Lynn had been sworn to secrecy about the envelopes and small packages that Lamar agreed to deliver. He knew Mama would have a heart attack if she knew all the candy, silly putty, and comic books they were giving him.

The bus was beginning to get crowded. Lynn and her mother always stood when it was crowded. Lynn pushed toward her mother. Mama said it built character to be able to stand up in a bus. Lynn thought differently as she watched the white woman and children quickly take the open seats. Zenobia didn't want to rock any boats or have any coarse interludes. Her idea was standing gave them a quick exit if they needed one.

A middle aged, white man got on the bus. It was apparent he had just gotten off of work because he was filthy dirty from head to toe. He stood next to Lynn and her mother. The one thing that Zenobia and all of her siblings agreed on, was Lynn was talking in complete sentences at an incredibly young age; complete clear sentences. There was standing room only. The dirty man stood over Lynn and her mother holding the overhead rail and trying desperately to keep his balance. When the driver made a sharp turn, the man swayed into Lynn and her mother's direction. Lynn did not hesitate to loudly complain to her mother.

"Mommy, Mommy! Make this nasty man move. He smells terrible! He nasty Mommy, make him move."

Zenobia was terrified that the man would get angry. She quickly tried to shush Lynn but her efforts were no match for the little girl. The more she tried, the louder Lynn got.

Lynn knew she had a captive audience so she made her voice louder.

"Mommy. I am going to have to take another bath today! Two baths in one day not because I got dirty, because this man right here is dirty. Momma…"

Lynn's voice cut off as the man reached into his pocket. Pockets were hideaways for knives and weapons. Being the only black people on the bus, the other riders seemed to be puckering their lips in scrutiny of this young mother and her sassy little girl. Mama stood frozen. She reached in her pocket for something to protect herself with. All her fingers could find was her house key.

"Dear Lord, take us fast!" her mother said under her breath as she put Lynn in a bear hug, both arms around her mouth.

But the man didn't seem angry at all. In fact, he was smiling.

He pulled out a five-dollar bill. He handed it to Zenobia and said:

"Buy that pretty little girl some candy. She's right. I am nasty dirty. I wouldn't want to stand next to me in a crowded bus."

Zenobia was stunned. She knew she had to accept that money since it was such a kind gesture. She thanked the man and was relieved to hear the hiss of the brakes as the bus slowed to a stop. She grabbed Lynn's hand and dragged her from the bus. But Lynn resisted,

"Mommy. This is not our bus stop. We need to go past the big church and..." But Zenobia was wrenching her arm off to step down. "My arm, Momma!" Lynn was screaming and beginning to cry. Her mother looked down at her with tears in her eyes.

"My dear baby girl," Zenobia said breathlessly. "We must never comment on someone else's appearance. Why, that man might have not been so nice! He could have slapped your mouth or done worse. Girl, you must not EVER comment on a white person's appearance. Ever. Or anyone else for that matter. Do you hear me?"

"Ok. Mommy please don't cry," Lynn said, as her mother collapsed on the bench and buckets of tears came out of her eyes. She motioned to Lynn to come in for a squeeze and Lynn let her mother hold her until she was all cried out.

They took a cab the rest of the way home with the $5 the man had given them.

"Is this the straw that broke the camel's back?" Zenobia asked herself while riding in the back of the cab. Chicago is just too big and dangerous for a mother and young children to be living alone. She was going to need to get out of here soon. She hated the thought of leaving her well-paying job. She would start looking at other places to live. Gary, Indiana was up and coming and had a slightly better reputation than Chicago. But really, wasn't it just an extension of the South Side?

She was going to think long and hard on this. Maybe they could make it work here, but she didn't know anything about the Black Disciples until the next day.

It was a Saturday morning. The kids were sleeping a little later and Zenobia was preparing the laundry basket and finishing her grocery list. The children brought their clothes to her in the kitchen. She took the time to shake out each item. She had been fooled before with inky messes in the wash and over the other clothes.

When she shook Lamar's clothes, penny candy came out first. Hard and still wrapped, it clattered to the floor. Next came coins in all sizes from nickels to quarters. They rolled under the table. In one pocket alone she wrestled out a yoyo, two baseball cards, a wad of chewed gum, and a pixie stick.

"Humph," Zenobia muttered. She knew that her son didn't have the chance to go to the store. He went to school blocks away and walked with all the kids in one large group from the bus stop

"Now, where did all of this stuff come from?" She mused. Knowing her son Lamar, he would not give a straight answer. He had already learned that lesson from the streets. She would have to catch him in a trap.

The kids wandered into the kitchen when they woke up, each leaning into their mother for a wraparound hug. Lamar was the last one in.

When they had assembled, Zenobia said:

"I have good news for you children! The laundry basket this morning was full of candy and toys! It must have been a fairy at work because I know none of you could have possibly gone to the store and bought this stuff. That would require money, which you do not have. So everyone, go ahead and pick three things that you would like. It's quite a pile."

Zenobia laughed happily and appeared to admire the collection of things brought before her. She kept an eye on Lamar. His eyes shot straight to Lynn, who simply shook her head no. His somber little face twitching as if a devil sat on one shoulder and an angel on the other. Finally, he burst out,

"Wait! That belongs to me!"

Lynn began to watch her mother finish setting the trap. She knew who was giving Lamar the candy. He even shared some with her not to tell. Mama better not pull her into this.

"Well, son," Momma said. "Do you care to explain just where did this come from?"

"I did some work for Mr. Gray last week," Lamar said, looking at the floor. His green eyes were clouded over. He knew he could not look straight at Momma and tell a lie. Lynn knew Momma knew it too.

"Some work?" Momma asked, "Just what did you do for Mr. Gray?"

"I picked up sticks in his yard."

"Sticks in his yard?" Momma was almost laughing. "Let's go take a look."

Of course, Lamar and Zenobia weren't the only ones going over to Mr. Gray's in their pajamas. Lynn and her two sisters got in line after them, wondering how this was going to end.

Lamar was dragging behind his fast stepping mother. She turned around and said,

"Yes, Son? Is there something else you want to tell me, maybe?"

"Momma? I didn't tell you the truth. I didn't do work for Mr. Gray."

"I see. And just where did this candy and junk come from?"

Lamar pointed to a group of boys hanging around the basketball court at the end of the apartments. Some were playing and some were just milling around waiting for some action. There were several, furtively watching them as Lamar carried out the conversation with his mother.

"Let's get in the house," Momma said and she was practically running. "Lamar, you know who those boys are, right? Tell me who they are?"

"Darnell," Lamar started.

"Not their first names! Lamar! You know that is the Black Disciples gang. What did the Black Disciples want with a little boy like you? You need to be honest here, son."

Zenobia knew far more than the children about how this gang, in particular, groomed younger kids to do odd jobs for them. Lynn was watching her mother with shock and apprehension. What did they want with Lamar?

"They said it was extra," Lamar said.

"Extra?" Zenobia was agitated. "What do you mean 'extra'?" She shrieked.

"Well," Lamar swallowed "They said if I took an envelope down to the corner store, the man there would give me a bag to put some candy and stuff in."

"What was in the envelope?" Zenobia probed.

"I dunno. They told me not to look."

"Just how many times have you made these trips? Four? Ten? How many?"

"Mama," Lamar said calmly, "I only did it one time."

Lynn and her sisters collectively watched her mother march over to the phone. The dial spun rapidly as she put in the numbers. Was she calling up the Black Disciples?

"Mother, this is Zenobia. We are taking you up on your offer. We will be coming to Michigan by the end of the week. If it's alright with you and Daddy, we'll stay in your little house at the farm. Please tell me if this will put you out."

Lynn knew this phone call had been a long time coming and was as relieved as her mother when she heard her grandmother's jubilant HALLELUJAH coming through loud and clear.

Just like that, they left Chicago behind. Lynn wasn't sure if there would be an ice cream truck or if they would open the hydrants in the summer. She wondered where they would go to sit on Santa's lap since there weren't any large stores where they were headed. She did know that her grandparents loved them all and it would be wonderful to leave the doors unlocked and smell the clean fresh air that was all around.

She figured when she was grown, she could always go back to Chicago. What could that little town of Heaven offer her? As long as they were together, she knew she would be all right.

Lisa

Summer nights brought wet, heavy air oozing through the screens. Windows were thrown wide open as if gaping mouths gasping for air. It was the sizzling doldrums of the summer season. Even the big lake whispered with only an occasional puff of cooled breeze. Sleeping was impossible. But up here in Michigan no one complained about heat because in a blink winter would arrive. Summer was meant to be savored.

After Thanksgiving, Lake Michigan delivered and kept the promise of Lake Effect snow. During that time of year every day was gray. Stratus clouds blanketed the sky and the sun was a coveted stranger. For three months the town dug out from overnight snowfall not in inches but feet. Front end loaders piled snow in parking lots and up and down the boulevard. The walls were stacked several feet high, making it difficult to see the road from the houses. Great mountains of frozen waves stretched out into the lake as far as the eye could see. Snow days were likely to close schools in January and February. Sledding hills and ice skating were not for the weak of heart. The weather seemed to be relentless and full of the smell of wet wool and mildewed boots.

During this time the summer population shrunk from

25,000 to about 8,000. Heaven's year-rounders liked to take advantage of every minute that passed in the summer. With the sun's light lingering until at least 11:00 p.m., softball games, bike rides, swimming, and playing with neighborhood kids seemed endless. Fall came abruptly. One held their breath when the maple tree at the top of the hill showed hints of red up near the top. Soon, other trees would follow, changing from green to red, orange, and yellow. It was time to stock up and be ready to spend life inside.

I am not thinking about that now, Lisa told herself, as her brain kept bothering her to process. This tossing and turning in the damp sheets was getting her nowhere. She got up, went through the hall, and unlocked the front door. The stars twinkled brightly over the lake on her walk to the bench on the bluff. Tonight she listened to the waves and watched clouds flash with heat lightning as she quietly went about capturing fireflies in her hands. The world seemed large and filled with opportunity.

Insulated in small town life meant you knew pretty much everyone. If they weren't your actual friends, you knew who they hung around with. You knew groups that went out to the Red Carpet for dinner or the resort floor show. You even knew or had heard about people who stayed in the town and entered the dark bars whose owners never gave away the identity of their customers. There were country people and city people. Lake living people and farm loving people; church people or synagogue people. Mostly though, there were people whose families put down stakes long ago and, although some children flew the coop for larger cities and universities, many stayed put enjoying the familiar pace of life. Lisa knew it was too small of a place for her. She wanted to blow this pop stand someday. The need to validate her autonomy was great. She longed to be known for her accomplishments and ideas.

Looking west at the occasional lights peeping out now and then on the horizon, it was clear that people were out there fishing. The lights from fishing trawlers formed little circles and were signs that they were catching "messes" of running perch, or larger salmon hunkering low, or maybe schools of steelhead in a certain area. Lisa imagined the haggard fishermen who needed to cast their nets through the night to sell by morning to Jentsen's Fishery. At dawn, the fishery boat would head back toward the lighthouse and the channel, its smoke stack belching out black smoke. Hundreds of squawking seagulls cavorting to and fro as in competition for a random scrap, squabbled about the boat. Smaller trawlers followed the big boat in. It was a morning fishermen's parade.

Hopefully, the catch was good. Uncle Vern liked to be the first in line when the perch were running. He liked to tell his friends that he had the freshest mess anyone had ever seen. He bought dozens of perch and carried them home wrapped in a newspaper. Lisa set the scenario up in her mind. Aunt Sis would receive the package and immediately call Lisa's mother, who was like a daughter to her. *"Bring the family tonight for supper! Messes of perch!"* She'd say.

With her mouth watering, she hoped they would get a call today. She and Jane were learning how to work the deep fryer. They would plug it in and stand and watch for the indicator light to turn red; it made up a red eye on a scary face etched in front of the fryer. It looked like a devil and they squealed when the eye appeared. Then, they would each pick up a perch filet and sink it into the bowl. Dripping white with batter, the key was to gently lay it atop the others until Auntie would deem the basket full. With Sis' assistance, the girls would take turns slowly lowering it into the hot grease. It sputtered and sizzled as it fried and when the basket was lifted, it was immediately turned over all onto a newspaper covered cookie sheet. Salt and pepper shakers, the silver ones with handles, finished the golden crispy goodness. They'd repeat the prep and fry several dozen fish as the family gathered in the dining room. Mountains of french fries, hand cut earlier, would also go in the fryer. As soon as the last load was pulled out, Sis announced retirement time for the man in the fryer.

It was nice to reflect on good family times.

A cloud moved slowly over the full moon as she shook the happy thoughts from her head. Looking at it gave her a mental image of a black and white movie featuring Lon Chaney, Jr. He had just changed into the Wolfman and looking out from behind a tree, he raised his head and howled like a wolf. Too many scary movies hosted by Father Hambring in the Catholic Church basement could keep her awake for days. Monsters like Frankenstein or Dracula were brought to the screen by the priest on Saturday afternoons for free. That is, they were, until the incident.

It happened last spring and it caused him to shut down altogether. Lisa hated to even think about it. For Father Hambring to stop showing his prized horror movies to St. Leonard's kids meant that something bigger than his ego had taken the wind out of his sails. You would think he could handle a little unruliness from a group of eight or nine-year-old kids. Turns out, the group that attended that day of the "incident" had left him completely powerless.

Actually, he closed the doors early. He heard a group of public school kids were making plans to sabotage his movie day. The problem arose from the previous week when he shamed Chuckie Stimmin in front of the group. Chuckie was a bit of a pest but he was harmless. He never did anything with intentional malice. Father kicked him out and called him "a dull retarded boy." What the priest hadn't counted on was the fact that Chuckie had a lot of friends. He threatened to get the priest back for his mistreatment. He yelled he would be sending the whole Zone to the movies the following week.

Father laughed the threat off but it was in the back of his mind most of the week. It was frightening for a priest, really, when vows of sovereignty and kindness were ruffled by a group of people whose ethnicity spoke to a deeper soul than religion. He had justified segregation his whole life. More than this was the fact that Father Hambring had no idea how to contain a group of non-parishioners he couldn't intimidate or shame into behaving. Further, he was scared to death of doing or saying something that might set off a race problem in the small town of Heaven.

It made him uneasy as the youngsters began arriving in groups of fours and fives; kids he had never seen before. Most of them were African American. He looked out the windows at the sidewalk above the church basement. There was Chuckie Stimmin and he was pointing at him. When Chuckie saw he'd been noticed, he jabbed both middle fingers in the air before popping a perfect wheelie and racing off on his Stingray.

Something began to smolder deep inside the priest. His bigotry and feelings of entitlement long buried since taking his vows, were coming to the surface. He silently prayed to accept and overcome this challenge.

But there were way too many kids at the penny candy counter. Wax lips, candy buttons, Dotz, Charleston Chews, and little wax root beer bottles were creating a frenzy. No one stood in an orderly line. It was like a scene from the trading floor of the New York Stock Exchange at the closing bell.

As he stood there, all six foot three of him, looking through his black horn rimmed glasses, he scratched the small halo of gray hair on the back of his head. Another group of seven or eight boys and girls had come in stamping down the linoleum stairs and pushed up to the candy counter. They were well past the start time. Behind them, still more black kids were entering as if a "second wave." The little church basement was fuller than it had ever been for the free movies. The place was starting to pulse.

Father Hambring had never planned to entertain colored kids. He tried to keep an open mind, but his family had been from southern Indiana and what could he say? He was a product of the '50s. A good deal of folks he knew thought like he did. It was better to separate races in casual settings. It was the best way for people to get along. That's how he liked it. Now, as a priest he wanted to walk in the shoes of Jesus. He hoped that he could stay deeply rooted in his faith. He wiggled his feet in his shoes as if to strengthen his resolve.

There was an unsafe feeling in the room now. Loud and seemingly unafraid of new situations, the late group clamored over to the candy counter. They took no notice of the man in the long black dress. Father had put his hands on his hips as he waited for the kids to finish buying their candy.

"Hey boys and girls!" He shouted, "hurry up and get seated. These movies start at 1:30 not a minute later." He looked up at the clock which showed 1:47 PM. He might have to cancel the cartoon.

The kids from the Zone kept right on picking out their candy. This was something every kid did and looked forward to. Why did it seem so wrong and out of place with them?

There was a lot of squeaking and scraping of chair legs as "regulars" began to look over at who had breached their perimeter and why the cartoon hadn't begun. Heads were turning and long, knowing stares were being exchanged. Why were these kids even here? Outliers. They presented a whole new layer of apprehension. The chair kids began to whisper amongst themselves. Who could have possibly invaded their closed little parochial bubble?

A hubbub arose over by the candy. Robbie, an eighth grade boy, was selling today. Each week an altar boy was snagged the previous Sunday to sell candy at the movies. It was usually an easy job and meant a day off serving Mass on Sunday. The altar boys clamored for a chance to sleep in and eat free candy. But today would ruin it for future workers. The new kids were loading up on candy. Even at a penny, their amounts were approaching dollars!

Robbie had handed out the first brown bag and said:

"That will be 45¢."

"Forty-five cent? I thought these movies were free!" The newcomer shouted, indignant that he had been misled.

All heads turned to watch Robbie quietly trying to explain that the candy cost money. The movies were free. He was silently beseeching the priest for help, but he wasn't getting any assistance. One of the kids from the public school gave Robbie a five-dollar bill, although whether it was willingly or out of fright will never be known. With relief on his face, Robbie took the last order from the group and put the CLOSED sign up.

Sucking on jaw breakers and Sweet Tarts, the new kids kept coming up for more. After seeing the sign that said "Open at Intermission", they resolved to be first in line as they went back to the rows of chairs. Now the kids were streaming from the candy station and wanted seats together. They demanded that seats be cleared so they could sit with their friends. The St. Leonard kids were only too happy to move away from them. It was noisy and the throng just wasn't settling. They walked around looking for the bathroom. Some began playing Monkey in the Middle while throwing bags of M & Ms over unsuspecting player's heads. It felt like something was going to happen and it wasn't going to be good. Father Hambring tried to corral the restless herd back to the folding chairs.

"Everyone needs to take seats!" He growled with a booming voice that was meant to intimidate.

Lisa had never seen Father Hambring so indecisive. He looked like he was brand new at this rodeo. But she knew he certainly was not. He was a man that liked to have everything under his complete control. If it wasn't, you better not be in the wake of his anger. Knowing this made the St. Leonard kids tense as the new kids were asserting themselves loudly. It seemed as if someone was about to press the GO button to release the atomic bomb. He must have felt this too because the new group wasn't listening to him at all.

Father gave a warning, "I don't *have* to show these movies. They are my *private* collection," he said looking sternly beneath his tufted eyebrows. "You will be expected to remain in your seats or you will be asked to leave."

Satisfied that he had regained the upper hand, he gingerly took the first film from the canister and rigged it up. It was "Frankenstein Meets the Wolf Man."

Lisa nestled into her seat next to Billy and Pat. It is going to be okay, she told herself. Everyone is going to watch this scary movie. The priest turned off the lights. The group seemed settled in. The first few scenes were frightening precursors for what was to come next. Then there was a lull. The momentum slowed and that probably wasn't good for crowd control.

The black and white filmmaker had obviously settled on more of a plot line, but nobody in that church basement wanted to watch a woman faint or people talking in a weird fake British accent. The first ping of a jaw breaker hit the projector. The priest jumped up from his perch and strode to the back. He had no way of knowing who threw the candy, so he stood, thinking he might have a better vantage point to nip this uprising in the bud. He kept his eyes peeled and waited.

All the kids were waiting now. No one was watching the movie anymore. You could cut the anxiety with a knife. This must be what war is like, Lisa thought to herself. Just waiting for the first shot.

After some heckling, the crowd quieted down again. Frankenstein had regained their attention. The monster arrived on the scene just in time. Father Hambring breathed a sigh of relief, hoping he could make it to 3:30 PM and the end of this day without incident. In fact, a full five minutes passed with only a few reminders to stay seated. The priest went back to the projector.

Lisa would remember the day as calm with a storm building. Like when distant thunder and lightning flashed and echoed off the lake bank well before arriving on shore. The melee began small, as if with the sprinkling of the first raindrops. A Sweet Tart thrown here, a Milk Dud thrown there. Then the steady exchange of jaw breakers hitting their targets. Finally, there was a total cloudburst. The kids in the front row began screaming in pain. Holding their heads, ears, cheeks, or other exposed body parts, they were being peppered with hard candy.

"Ow! Hey! What's going on?" The screams were becoming louder. Movie-goers were standing now and turning around; retaliating in an unprecedented candy food fight the likes that had never been seen or imagined before. It had become a free-for-all. Candy wax lips and sour balls sailed by as Father Hambring finally jumped into action. He flipped the switch on the running reel. It stopped with a snap.

"Someone turn on the lights!"

But the only light in the room was the projector light on the screen. Everybody was frozen.

He swore and grabbed his film reel off the projector and threw it in its case. His movie collection was his most prized possession and he would take care of it first.

The candy fight was intensifying. Lisa was wondering why Father Hambring was taking so much time to put his movie away. There needed to be order and authority. This guy was not coming through. Kids were crying, some were bleeding, while still others were happily engaged in an all-out rumble.

But when Lisa checked out the priest, confident he would come through with his usual fire and brimstone, she realized that he was trying to get control of himself. His face was beet red and scrunched up like the football coach at the high school when he called the team *knuckleheads*. Lisa began to back away. Father Hambring was not going to be her safe fortress. She had to find the stairs. He was going to blow!

He was a yeller and thought nothing of belittling kids in front of others. She had seen him angry a number of times.

Once, he had stopped Mass in the middle of the consecration -the most holy part- and said plainly:

"Tim Serek! Get the hell down from that balcony. You have no business being up there. I will wait for you to come to this front pew and sit. Right now, dammit. Are you so stupid, you think I didn't see you?"

The whole congregation twisted around in their seats to

see a red-faced ten-year-old boy turn and go crashing down the balcony stairs and straight out the door. Mr. and Mrs. Serek had not moved and sat through the rest of the Mass, their faces scarlet with embarrassment. Tim never came back into the church. Father muttered:

"Some parents need to step in and discipline their children before it's too late."

Another time when Principal Sister Michael Mare asked him to speak to the students about their bad behavior, he made his point with clear enthusiasm by pounding a meter stick over and over on the podium. He must not have understood his own strength because before anyone knew it, the stick busted in pieces and a shard landed squarely in Tommy Mayflower's eye. The priest looked at Tommy, who was holding his eye trying not to cry and said, "You wait until you get God's punishment. That will make this look like an eyelash!"

Probably his most angry time was when Bobby Foster put a tack on Sister's chair and she sat down on it. No one was allowed to go home that afternoon until the rat came forward. Father was called in to interrogate and Bobby thought he was doing the right thing by owning up. Well, he was wrong, because Father Hambring spread a bag of hard navy beans on the floor.

"Kneel," the priest said. Bobby reluctantly knelt. His smirky smile changed to instant agony. His forehead was dripping large drops of perspiration and his face was pasty when an hour had finally passed and he was allowed to get off the beans.

Those previous flashes of anger appeared to be mild. Father Hambring was at the top of his angry meter now. Lisa had never seen anyone look like him. As if in slow motion, someone picked up a chair and threw it at the candy counter shattering the glass. There was a shocked moment as everyone stood stock-still.

The priest took two large strides to get to the light switch. He picked up the one of the Zone boys by the scruff of his shirt collar and started pushing him up the steps. To the others, he screamed,

"You NiG-G-ers! Get out of here!"

For a split second, when he said that word, Lisa felt as if all the air had left the room. She was dazed and likely in shock.

That word!

No one was allowed to say it! It was hateful. It was a sin! It was right up there with the F-word. She looked at the priest and saw a vein bulging out on his neck. He looked just like the Frankenstein monster carrying the body of the little girl.

"Git. You are never to set foot here again!" He was bellowing and stomping them off like you would a mad dog.

Scrambling up the stairs with the rest, Lisa did her best not to get trampled. She saw a girl about her age, wearing the exact same sweater, slip on the step. She would certainly be hurt under all the feet. She reached her and pulled her up by the braids.

"Come this way!" She yelled.

The little girl was frightened but she was by no means terrified. It looked like this was a fine adventure for her. Lisa took her down the tunnel that connected the school to the church basement. She opened up the door and let the girl out.

"I'm Lynn Parris. What's your name?"

"I'm Lisa Palma, and I am sorry for what he said to you."

"It's okay." Lynn said "I've heard that word before. Is it always so crazy here at this church? I have never seen so many disrespectful white children!"

"I think there were plenty of kids doing the wrong thing," Lisa said, somewhat hurt by Lynn's insinuation that her group had started things. "Nothing like this has ever happened before."

Lynn ran off to catch up with her group.

Lisa thought "she's just like me" as she walked faster to catch up with the St. Leonard's kids who were spilling down the beach steps across from the school to discuss, with absolute adrenaline rants, the steps leading to the moment the priest had "lost it." They were making predictions of his firing. She tagged along behind her brother.

Personally, she was traumatized by what had just taken place. How would she ever look at Father Hambring again? How could she confess her sins to him when he had committed a grave sin right in front of her? Would that little brown girl get into trouble because she had gone to these movies?

But on Monday, it was as if nothing had happened. Kids that went home and told parents of the melee were told to keep a lid on it. The priest was just doing what he had to do. She wasn't sure how she felt about it all. It made her feel like it was wrong to call those kids that word, yet no one was really acting like it was.

Several of the parents went to talk to Father Hambring. She thought it was to address his behavior on that Saturday movie day. It was not. The parent group wanted to post a "parent guard" at the doorways so only approved children could attend the movies.

But Father had been reluctant to discuss it. He told them he hadn't made up his mind if he would continue Saturday movies.

Suddenly reality hit. Lisa had been sitting on the bench much too long. Yawning, she scratched a new mosquito bite and trudged past the empty lot to her house feeling like a ghost in the night. Secrets and questions always came to her on these late evenings.

Like, what was wrong with those public school kids? Were the kids who lived in the Zone taught to hate white kids? Why did they have to throw stuff and ruin those movies? Or, why did she feel a little dirty with them going there, like she had after walking around at the Van Buren County Fair? Sister Rosina told her class in first grade that they were the lucky ones. What did that even mean? Lucky and white?

Crawling back into her top bunk, Lisa thought on the subject of being one of the lucky ones? Why would God not choose everyone to be lucky?

Lynn

Although they lived near Lake Michigan, the fifth largest lake in the world, some kids with homes miles inland had never seen it, let alone stuck a toe into its refreshing, unsalted water. Some people were simply too busy to go through the hassle of rounding up a picnic basket, swimming towels, lotions, bathing caps, and snacks. Instead, parents who worked during the hot summer days brought home kiddy pools, or had the kids run through the sprinkler or the hose. Most newcomers or inland families were never taught to swim. Heaven's high school offered swimming lessons at the high school pool a few times a year. But, if you didn't live in a mansion on Lakeshore Boulevard or in the sweet little subdivisions tucked along the bluff, you probably wouldn't take swimming lessons.

Summer at the shore was mostly for tourists anyway. People used their two-week vacations to rent out a cottage on the water and spend their days swimming and building sandcastles. A secret that many visitors discovered was that the sand of the Great Lakes was made from thousands of tiny, multicolored rocks that had been pummeled to fine granules. For those who had only visited salt water beaches, where sand consisted of powdery, sharp fragments of shells, the lake sand had a magical quality. It was not dirty with sea plants or sea creatures. Except for the time of the alewife die-off, the beach's only threat was directly from humans. Public beaches were littered with pop bottles, snack cans, tampon containers, cigarette butts, and a multitude of undetermined styles of trash.

Heaven's lifeguards came at sunrise and combed the beach with an old set of bed springs dragged behind a tractor. The big pieces of garbage piled up inside them and a city worker would follow with their specialized golf carts, donated by the Heaven Country Club, and scoop the stuff into a huge box in the back of the cart. The seagulls scavenged those caches for odd bits of this or that. Tourists made them aggressive and they would take a sandwich right out of your hand if you didn't eat it fast enough.

Things moved slow for kids in the summer. Groups of friends who reached the age of emancipation (which in Heaven was around eight or nine) biked into town for ice cream or Cokes. Penny candy was sold at the G.E. Murphy dime store downtown from a large glass case. Candy was placed in white paper bags. Often overflowing, the bags proved too small to hold the stash of candies. Perfectly good candy pieces were lost to the sidewalk outside the front door. Mary Janes or salt water taffy were often reclaimed with the five second rule. Watchers walked around the store and when a bagful of candy went out the door, they made their way outside to pick up anything that had dropped.

Most children that were "natives or year-rounders" signed up for the organized recreation programs at one of three parks.

There they would have a park director, usually a college student on summer break, leading activities for the kids for the entire day. The program was free to the community, as if to say, "Thanks for sharing the beach with the tourists." The park directors and their assistants served as organized babysitters for five-year-old kids and older.

The three parks were strategically placed. Their names were: Lake Park, Tot Park, and Moon Park. Lake Park: for the kids that lived at the lakeshore. Tot Park: for younger children of preschool ages. Moon Park: for kids who lived in and around the factory district and butting right up next to the Zone.

Lynn called Moon Park, simply the Park. Her cousins lived right down the block and she loved going there when visiting from Chicago. There were many people with visiting family who took advantage of the organized programs. There were serious basketball tournaments between the Lake Park and Moon Park. Often contentious, each park built up to the competition with cheerleaders, homemade signs, and park shirts to show pride. They took turns hosting the week long tournament, a day of games at Moon Park followed by a day of games at Lake Park. By the end of the week, many adults from all over town would stroll down to stands or watch from parked cars as the talented boys from each park battled to the finals.

Lynn loved going to the park with her cousins. There was a real sense of community when the parks squared off. Better still, was the fact that many times the boys from Moon Park whaled on the boys from Lake Park. When tempers flared the fans stayed in the stands. Some pushing and shoving would lead to name-calling, but for the most part, the teams reconciled knowing when they'd been outplayed It was the one thing that reminded Lynn of Chicago neighborhoods. The sense of who you were was derived mostly from the neighborhood you hailed from.

But Heaven was a town so unlike Chicago. Things moved fast there. If you wanted candy, you walked to the corner store and in a few minutes, you had candy. If you wanted to go to the movies, you could pick from more than five movie houses, all within short walks from your neighborhood. Everyone was surrounded by loving family of some sort, plenty of cousins, and lots of church family. But in Heaven, cousins lived right alongside grandparents. Running over to sleep or spend time together was a walk of less than three minutes.

Last year in Chicago, Uncle Ed, her father's cousin managed the Cabrini-Green projects. Everyone knew and respected him so there was never any drama. Lynn remembered that one of her favorite movies, *Cooley High*, was filmed in those projects and her cousins attended school there during the time of the filming. They asked Lynn and Lamar to watch with them outside the "Set". It was funny to see the real cops and the actor cops interacting. Sirens and firetrucks always lifted the heads of children playing, people talking, or people watching and it got to be a game whether the siren was a movie siren or belonged to the Chicago PD. Heaven's police station had three cars. They were easily discernible by make and color. The force was made up of mostly guys who grew up there. They let people slide for minor infractions. The Zone was a place they liked to leave as is.

In Chicago, there was always the hustle and bustle of cars, buses, and El trains. Neighborhoods tended to segregate back then. If you saw any white people, they were usually in uniform and you probably were not too happy to see them. Efforts were being made to upgrade the areas, but it wasn't happening quickly.

So, when her mother said they were headed to Michigan, not to Gary or another house in Chicago, Lynn was filled with hope. For as long as she could remember, her mother had been the breadwinner. Sometimes, in those early days, it was hard to decide who was living at her house and who was just visiting.

Mama's generous spirit had run out. When a "down on his luck" friend robbed her of all her good jewelry and silverware, that was it; well, that and the Black Disciples. Mama said she'd know when it was time. She wanted more for herself and her kids. Heaven could give her a brighter future. She had just finalized her divorce and was looking ahead for once.

Lynn's grandparents bought sixty acres of land in a rural area about ten miles east of Heaven. They built a small, one-room house on the land and, realizing it was just too small, built a larger, 4-bedroom in front of it. They were called the "big" house and the "little house." Lynn loved being near her grandparents.

Her grandmother had many talents. One talent she had that Lynn loved the most was storytelling. She could tell a story so clearly that it made you feel like you were there. One of Lynn's favorite stories was of how her grandparents met. When grandmother told the story, the children quietly listened usually on their beds or at her feet. She had a gentle way of leading them into her stories. That way, they were good and quiet when the juicy parts came.

So, as she began, they nestled down, and listened. It had been told many times before but never changed. It laid down a foundation for them of how they were and who they had come to be.

"*Children, you know that I have a twin sister?*" She began. "*She lives in Tennessee. Well, when we were but four years old, our mama died. Can you imagine? Teeny tiny girls growing up without a mama. Oh, I wish I could remember my mother more, but what I remember most is the way she made a rhubarb pie and how she smelled of lavender and flowers.*

Well, my father couldn't raise a family alone, so right away he married my stepmother, Juanita. They became a blended bunch, adding three boys. His father, 'Papa' we called him, lived next door. Our houses were close but we had acres and acres of land where my father would plant his crops. They called him a "share cropper" because the land wasn't all the way his. He shared the crops and part of the profits with the land owner. It was a good arrangement and we kids pitched in to help.

When Papa was around he often spoke to us in different languages. He had been born in France and had mastery of 11 different languages, and he let us know that every time we spoke. He liked to change a word or phrase and ask us what it meant. He and my father often spoke French, but my Daddy knew only 7 languages.

You see, my grandfather was known as an orator. Back in those days, few black men were allowed to do public displays in the South, but once you made it to the Yankee states, your speeches were meaningful, especially among abolitionists. Abolitionists didn't like slavery at all. They believed that all people should be able to live on the land, equally. Of course, the black abolitionist best known for his writing and speaking was Fredric Douglass.

Well, one day, Papa was heading to a meeting at the Lodge. He was the Grand Chancellor of the Knights of Pythias, and a very honorable man. Well, he got up to the podium to start his oration and he looked into the audience and there before him was Fredric Douglass! Your Papa stood up taller and finished his speech with gusto. Afterward, Mr. Douglass approached him and told him what a solid and strong orator Papa was. He asked him if he would like to join him on a few upcoming destinations. They ended up speaking at several places together and your great grandfather even wrote some of Fredric Douglass' speeches with him".

Grandmother always paused at this point and got the picture of Papa and Fredric Douglass off the mantel. "TO Nelson Reynolds, a gentleman and a scholar. Respectfully, Fredric Douglass." The children would each be able to hold the framed picture before grandmother put it back on the mantel.

"Children, your great grandfather was a famous man. Why, did you know there was a park named after him in Pulaski, Tennessee? It was filled with trees and ponds and we would often have our Sunday dinners in the park.

Let me get back to my story, I was enrolled in Finishing School in Pulaski, Tennessee at the time. My father would bring me into school in the morning, do chores in town, or have meetings with other businessmen. One day, while in a business meeting, he was talking about the trials of having daughters. I was starting college at the business school. He simply did not like the idea of his daughter staying in town alone in strange surroundings. I was quite a beautiful girl back then. Anyway, Joseph Madry, the man he was meeting with, said he has daughters and they would love it if I used their home as a base during the school days. It solved a load of problems, and the arrangements were quickly made. I went home nearly every night, at first to help with chores but as my studies became more demanding, I began to sometimes stay at the Madry's more often.

Children, I have always been known for my dreams of premonition. One night, I was bone tired. I had an accounting class that made my head hurt from looking at numbers all day. When I got to the farm, I laid down to rest. I fell into a deep sleep. The dream I had was of walking up a green hill filled with flowers. At one point, I looked up and saw a beautiful woman coming down the hill with two buckets of milk on her shoulders. On one bucket was the letter "B" and the letter "J" was on the other bucket. The woman had two young boys running along beside her. When I woke up, I thought for a little bit about that dream, but there was so much going on, I pushed it to the side.

The months passed quickly and there wasn't much else to do but think about school. On the last day of that semester, I heard a hubbub of noise when I opened the door to the Madry's house in Pulaski. The family turned to look who was coming in the door. Joseph Madry stepped forward and said, "Kathleen, this is my son Ewell. He is home on leave from the army." Well, I was somewhat bashful but I must say I loved a man in uniform. I stayed for dinner that evening, I kept taking fast glimpses of Ewell. He had a full, happy laugh. I know he was looking at me too. His family adored him and if there is love at first sight, well, this could have been it.

After dinner, we walked down by the pond. Ewell's mother had been out of town visiting family. She rushed in too late for dinner. Excited to see her son, she came running down the hill calling his *name. He turned around and saw his mother and two young boys coming down the hill toward them. I will never forget that moment of déjà vu. It was as if the dream from months ago was unfolding. There was the woman coming down the hill. She didn't have milk on her shoulders but she was stunning. Her name was Janie Brown. The "J" and "B" from my dream were the initials of her name! The two boys were Ewell's brothers! Everything had clicked from the dream. I knew I was meant to be part of this family. It would be as Ewell's wife. I was meant to marry him and the dream just confirmed this.*

It was a magic moment."

Lynn's grandmother always ended the story that way and by then, the children were fast asleep.

Lisa

They say that Lisa's great grandfather, Alfred, had his pulse on the village of Glenn. Barely large enough to have a Post Office, Glenn had long been an area for visitors who really wanted to get away from it all. Since Alfred had the only barbershop in town, located in a room inside of his house, the news and gossip of Heaven (to the south) and Saugatuck (to the north) brought men flocking to his door. Trading eggs, live chickens, or produce in season for their haircuts or shaves, the barber shop was always crowded with three or four regular local folks that just needed a place to convene. Sometimes no one even got a haircut all day!

Visiting her great grandparents' house in Glenn was usually in answer to a call for help from Lisa's mother. The "farm" which really wasn't a farm, gave Carla the chance to unload a few of her kids for a week or two and lighten her burden at home. She usually would have Lisa go with the older two, while the twins and Jane stayed home.

Lisa loved it at her Grandma Lulu's house. It had a timeless charm and provided her with unconditional, strong love from her grandparents. Grandma Lu had a way of making each great grandchild feel unique and important.

There were so many things to love about a visit there. First, baking days. The house always smelled of yeast. Fresh bread, and mouthwatering surprises often awaited the children on their visits to Glenn. Pie Days were especially good times for teaching the finer points of baking. On these days while grandma masterfully constructed her pie crust, she would give the kids their own bits of crusts to place in tiny pie tins. They would put jam on them and bake them alongside grandma's large pies. The tiny pies were personal masterpieces. They came out of the oven burnished and warm in tiny tart pans that, it seemed, Grandma had kept for just that use.

She served the tarts or pies to them on the small table and chairs in which she had situated their mother when she was a girl. Grandma would politely turn away and grin when her great grandkids prepared to eat, for it was only when they bit into their "pies" that the children realized that there was not one thing about them that was similar to a real pie that Grandma made. They were lard and flour, rolling on the tongue rather more like cardboard with a gummy jam topping, and Grandma knew how disappointed they would be in their flavor. But she was giving them basic steps of pie dough making, knowing she could not waste the time making fillings. They lost interest too quickly. But Lisa felt it was wonderful to wear an apron- hers was the one with the apple print- and learn to measure from bins that were built right into grandma's kitchen cupboards by her Great Grandpa Alfred. The bins were huge and held sugar and flour. Sometimes a stray mouse or two would find its way into the bin. They were never alive. Most likely they had been in the bin for a while. Grandma simply scooped the lifeless bodies up with a big spoon and dropped them in the compost bucket.

After baking, time was often spent in the garden. Grandma Lulu grew and cross bred many different varieties of iris and lilies. Although she had no specialized education in science, never made it past the eighth grade, she knew more about creating a hybrid than most scientists did. This was great, and all, but it became more like manual labor at a prison when she oversaw the kids hoeing between the flower rows. The rock hard ground would cause reverberations up the arms. The sun beat down in a series of punches on heads with no hats. It seemed to take an eternity. Billy and Marcy would finish early and take off to play on the shady side of the house. There was a lily pond there surrounded by grape arbors that made a sort of magical green room. Huge goldfish the size of rabbits would swim to and fro in the pond. The kids caught slimy newts and salamanders that scampered out from behind and under the pond rocks. Grandma told them the pond was actually a fresh spring. It held cool water and there was a tin cup in the crotch of a small tree that was used to capture ice cold drinks. Lisa cried as she struggled to hoe her patch of lilies. She wanted to play with the others.

When she was sure the others were gone, grandma would get out of her metal chair, stained from sitting under the mulberry bush, and she would help Lisa finish. Later, she gave her the first snack of bread and butter and brown sugar before she called the others in for theirs. Grandma Lulu's love was not fractured. It felt like when the sun -after teasing with a few weak rays- came out full force to envelope with its warmth completely.

A strange thing when visiting Glenn, was noon meals were called "dinner," not lunch. The last meal of the day was "supper." Dinner meant the table was set with the Fiestaware dinner plates, small bowls for fruit, and side plates for salad. Silverware came from a wooden box and the napkins were cloth. Grandpa Alfred had already let Marcy choose the chicken from the dirt yard by the barn. While the kids were doing the chores, he was butchering. He came around the side of the barn where grandma sat and gave her a wink and she was gone for a few minutes. Somehow during that time, she had transformed the live bird into a large pan of chicken in bubbling gravy with dumplings on top. In the small bowl, grandma had identified the unrecognizable fruit as canned prunes. The salad was made from leaves snatched from the lettuce row in the garden. Several dark green leaves of Swiss Chard were mixed with a few Romaine leaves. It did not crunch like the Iceburg lettuce Mom used back home. Yet, the tomatoes ripened on the vine and the carrots extracted by their bushy tails made for a wonderfully fresh salad bursting with flavor. The buttermilk dressing lightly wetted the leaves.

Lisa watched her great grandparents as an observer might. Neither of them were handsome. Lulu had hooded eyes that made her appear sleepy. Her red lipstick was almost always chipping or wearing off her lips. She wore glasses with lenses so thick each eye looked as if it was in a magnifying glass. She had a soft and gentle laugh and at times a few witty jokes. She was the essence from which Lisa's life was grounded.

Grandpa Alfred, on the other hand, was a bit of a distant character. He looked as if he was drawn on a cartoonist table.

Sharp features for nose and chin. Squinty little eyes. He wore a straw hat with a clear green front piece to block the sun. In the barbershop, he wore a half hat called a visor. He was a jokester and his laugh exposed teeth in a pointed face like a small animal, maybe a fox. He died very early in Lisa's childhood. She remembered him for digging into her sides, hurting her but thinking he was tickling. She would stave off the tears with a smile and wiggle away whenever he wanted to frolic around.

Although they weren't called "siestas" there was a time after the big meal at noon to rest and rejuvenate. This was reading time. Lulu would sit in her big chair. Marcy, Billy, and Lisa would climb up onto her ample lap clinging to her for a snug spot like baby possums. She asked them to select their favorite stories for her to read then. Lisa loved "Mouse House." The story was of a mouse getting trapped in the junkyard by an overturned tea cup with night approaching. It was a very real fear she had, of being left behind with no one knowing. The end filled her with elation as the mother mouse searched and searched until she found her beloved Timmy. Marcy picked "The Wizard of Oz" but grandma just read a chapter at a time. The books were not like the movie. They were filled with a maniacal world of fantasy. Things in Oz were strange and the people were unlike anything Lisa ever wanted to meet. Billy chose "Long, Broad, and Quick Eye" about a band of super powered do-gooders. Long could make himself tall and walk to faraway places in just a few steps. Broad could make himself into a steel wall of limitless expanse. Quick Eye had such incredible eyes he could shoot a fly off an apple with a bow. He wore a bandana around his eyes because his acute vision made him miserable at times. The trio was constantly involved in adventures that required each of their skills. Grandma read each book with the inflection it required. From a tiny mouse to a seven mile wide man. If someone asked Lisa what her favorite place was, she would say grandma's lap when she read.

Once finished with reading, the kids would move to the bookshelf. There were several cigar boxes there filled with pictures that told the story of family and relationships. One grandchild held the box while the other two held the pictures, taking turns to hand them up to their grandmother. This was a travelogue of family history. Tin type photos were mixed in with sour or sad faces of families or couples. Grandma Lulu would explain the characters and setting of each picture. Sometimes, she would pause, like when she got to Charles. He was her son and Lisa's mother's father. He died at the age of 25 from meningitis. His wife, Dorothy, had been only 19 at the time. Grandma's eyes would mist over and then she would say something like… without that short marriage, I would never have had you to love.

Lisa's mother didn't grow up in a traditional family. At the time of her father's death, it was 1932. The Great Depression was deep and World War II was looming. A nineteen year old widow, Dorothy had a child she couldn't properly care for, so she gave her over to Lulu and Alfred to raise. She would spend the rest of Carla's childhood life coming and going. Although Lisa's mother yearned for the wholeness of a mother and father, she had something better. The love of her father's parents who had lost a son. Carla may not have ever felt like others who she went to school with or even her own cousins. But she knew she sat at the center of a circle of love.

Lynn

It hadn't taken her mother long to meet and marry William. Lynn supposed her mother needed the hope of a partner in raising and providing for the family. Mama and William lived at the *little* house by themselves when they first married, and Lynn and her siblings lived in the *big* house with their grandparents. It didn't take too long for the arrangements out at the farm to become too stifling for William. Time moved too slowly and he had no experience with farm work. Zenobia had agreed that they needed another income and they settled on a small house about a block from Moon Park.

After moving, the children still spent a good deal of time with their grandparents. As they became familiar with their new neighborhood, they stayed in town more often. William watched the children while his wife worked. Mostly that meant telling Lynn when to make lunch for everyone while he watched game shows on the little black and white television in the garage and drank beer.

It came as some surprise that her stepfather got a job. Weekends only. Ralph's Tavern.

Lynn knew Ralph's Tavern as the one bar in town that black

folks could have to themselves. Ironically owned by a white
man, this establishment was strictly for people of color, men
mostly. Although there were no signs to keep people out, most
year-rounders knew what determined the clientele of the establishment. It was a place to be comfortable among their own
community and spend their paychecks. Crisp, cold brews awaited
them at the sound of the factory whistles at 3:30 PM.

The bar featured a bare naked light bulb hanging straight
down its center. The wattage was little more than 40. The
wire, covered with an old, woven cloth cord wrap, resembled a
crooked snake. Apparently, the owner did not invest in updating
it much, often exclaiming that the place was worth more money
to him if it burned down. The front screen door was framed
in wood and painted with a patina of many shades of green. It
slapped shut with a loud bang like a flyswatter hitting a flat wall.
That sound stimulated the bar stool sitters to turn their heads.
Like a magnet several sets of eyes were pulled to the entrance.
New members would be checked out with the friend or foe
glance. Although many who were extra thirsty that day may be
weighing the odds of a free drink or two. If it was a regular, the
men would call out and cut up a little bit, a momentary break
in the otherwise somber sitting and staring persona they had
come to enjoy. Many tourists walked into Ralph's for a drink
not knowing what they would encounter on the inside. The
bartender would ask if the visitor would take a look around and
then decide if they wanted a drink. The braver ones would say, of
course they did. But as the silence of the room grew more and
more threatening, the single drink was gulped at a pace beyond

the sip. The bar seemed to hold its breath waiting for the slap of the door. It acted as a switch that brought instant waves of hooting and hollering.

Anyway, William got a job. The kids at home rejoiced. No more being watched by him. Mama spent her weekends recovering from her week at work. So it seemed like a great situation. But, William was a man who cooked up ideas to make money at no cost to himself.

One day, he came home with a woman.

"Ya'll this is Netti," he said in his company voice. "She is going to live here and be our maid. She will cook meals during the week so your mama doesn't have that burden. Ya'll are going to have to listen to her and do what she says."

Nettie looked around the kitchen. Her eyes were bloodshot and watery.

"Where are her things?" Lynn's mother asked. "Where will she sleep, in the garage?"

"What you mean things?" Netti scowled. "I am bringing what God gave me."

Zenobia was a Christian woman. She would not turn anyone away right away without a meal and a chance to rest.

"Oh! Sweet Jesus!" Mama said. "This is a very temporary arrangement, William."

William had done this several times in his short life as their stepfather. It was an easy side hustle and a way to make money. He knew almost everyone who got a disability check by their drinking patterns. On the days the checks came in, he would know just exactly who would come through the door to spend it at Ralph's. Disability checks were the easiest ones to get a cash out on. Netti got disability checks. In her not so sober moments, which was always, she would make William the payee on her checks. He brought her home so he could say he was giving her room and board. It was not exactly a lie, although he doubted it was quite the way the government intended it to be.

During the next few weeks, Lynn got a back story on Nettie.

Netti was a regular at Ralph's Tavern. One day, she just blew in the front door, like a dried leaf needing water. The men easily picked up on the fact that the clothes she wore never changed. She didn't seem to have a hygiene habit or take particular care in her appearance. She only had one thing on her mind, how am I gonna get another drink? Willie Portnoy was the first man who asked her if she did services for men. She smiled and said anyone will do anything for a price. Willie offered to buy her two drinks for a ten-minute Hoover vacuum treatment in the men's room. The other men watched with little interruption as Netti swayed back to the small, one-stall bathroom.

"Now, William," they began to buzz after the door was locked, "that is our only stall. You have got to get a different place for her to do her business. She can stay. Just find her a different spot."

The door to the bathroom unlatched and out stepped a smiling Willie Portnoy. "Bring this woman a shot of Wild Turkey!" He yelled so all would know and share in his triumph.

William walked back into the small storage room that had a safe and a few boxes of supplies. After moving things out of the way, he laid himself down. Plenty of room to sit or stand or lay. He thought. He decided to make this his "side, side hustle."

Netti and whatever man she was with could use this room for $5 for a ten-minute period. Over time he would double the price. He came back out and slipped the message to Willie and Nettie in a whisper. Netti was so smashed at this point, it didn't really matter what he told her. She met all his suggestions with a smile of appreciation.

The first few days were busy ones for Netti. She couldn't drink the amount of drinks she was earning. She asked William if he would just give her drinks for free, but William said that it would be illegal. So instead, suggested she give up her check to him and he would see about room and board.

Lynn thought about this clever, yet ugly way William used this woman. She didn't dare tell her mother, although she thought she probably had a pretty good idea of what was happening.

The amount of booze that Netti could put away amazed Lynn. The poor woman was more like a child than a maid. It made her wonder what could have happened in her life that was so bad that she never wanted to sober up to face it. Lynn heard she was 30 years old, and she sure didn't want to look wrecked like that when she reached her 30s.

Following Netti around the house during the day became Lynn's job. She wasn't home much after mama got home from work. Lynn undid much of Netti's damage, as she drunkenly knocked over things she was cleaning, or cleaned up after her cooking messes.

One day, coming in from school, Lynn found Netti laid out on the kitchen floor. The food in the pan on the stove was not recognizable. As she reached across her body to turn off the stove, Lynn was feeling less compassionate and more frustrated. Just because her step-dad was now the payee on the disability check didn't mean any of them were benefiting from Netti being there. She wasn't a clean person. To call her a maid and a cook was laughable. The house was too small. One bathroom for the whole family was not adequate even when Netti wasn't there. Not for a family of four, and certainly not for eight or nine people that William seemed to drag home on a constant basis.

It was Lynn's job to make sure the bathroom was picked up. But sometimes she just could not. Nettie had a habit of sitting on the toilet and leaning over to vomit on the floor. She would leave her mess and pass out wherever there happened to be an open spot. Lynn would follow her out and look in to check. Sure enough, Netti would have vomited, not neatly, mind you, but down the wall or across two walls. Lynn, knowing her mother would not have this in her home, would clean it up for her step-dad. He paid her a small amount so she kept quiet. She hated betraying her mother, but she learned there was a certain value in having a side hustle.

There would eventually be a final straw with Netti, Lynn thought. There always was with the people William brought by.

It came when cabbage was being boiled on the stove. Normally, Netti wasn't too horrible of a cook; it depended on her drunk meter. Somewhere back before she became a drunk, she learned the basics of cooking. But on this particular day, she was weaving and stirring on the stove. "Got to git the oil." She muttered to herself.

Lynn watched as Netti walked into the cleaning supplies and got out the lemon furniture polish. Its golden color actually looked a bit like corn oil, but surely she wasn't going to add that into the pot. As Netti undid the lid of the bottle, Lynn watched, horrified as she began to tip it, and she quickly took it out of her hands.

"Netti!" She cried. "That's furniture polish!"

Netti's eyes never changed. She looked at Lynn and said, "get the goddam oil then!"

That moment became the last straw for so many reasons. First, Lynn was tired. Netti made twice as much work for her. Second, if her mama knew all the things that went on in the house during the day, she surely would not stand for it, and make her leave. The only good thing was having Netti there took her stepfather's attention off of Lynn. He made excuses for touches he made by "accident." She was sure that he would get more physical with Netti gone and she got prepared mentally with a plan that would stop him in his tracks. She was much smarter than William. He had to know she was much more dangerous, too.

But the furniture polish incident, and the way she used God's name in vain had added to the already overflowing list of things. It was time to tell her mother.

Mama walked in that night, bone tired after a particularly long day. Lynn got her a cool drink, and sat down and asked her how her work was. Her mama held her in a brief hug. "Not a bad day. God is good," she said. "What's troubling my baby?"

"Mama. Netti made a bad mistake today," Lynn began.

"I am certain it won't be her last." Mama said

"Mama. She was going to pour the lemon furniture polish into the cabbage pot," Lynn said in barely an audible whisper.

"She what?" Mama cried.,"oh Lord no. Not anymore. Not my babies' health."

With that she gathered herself up in her fiercest pose. She found Nettie passed out in the backyard on a blanket.

"Get yourself up from there!" She demanded.

"You done working?" Netti asked.

"We can no longer have you living in our home, Netti. We have tried to help you through some tough times, but it's time for you to find another place. I will call the church and see if they have a bed for a night or two."

Netti didn't argue. Lynn wasn't quite sure she knew that mama was kicking her out.

"Would you like a bowl of cabbage?" Netti asked.

"You are leaving now." Mama said, "gather up your things, now."

Netti headed down the block to the Baptist Church. They knew her there and would take care of her until they couldn't. Likely two nights.

"What will you tell William?" Lynn asked, after Netti had been gone for a bit.

"Let's see how long it takes for him to notice." Mama chuckled.

Well, it didn't take William long at all to notice Netti was gone.

"Why'd you have to go and ruin our perfect income?" He

yelled. "Get a regular job, William." Mama had cried, "I am not having someone come in and poison my family. We don't need income like that."

With a sigh of relief, everyone cooled off for a few weeks and the routine became more regular. Lynn was cooking these days. Her grandmother taught her all the good family recipes, and she developed a flair for it. Her siblings were rarely late when she was putting food on the table.

William was still simmering over the release of Netti and her check.

Lisa

Sunny Summer Wednesdays, while welcomed in Michigan, had some annoying qualities. First, they brought light through the windows much too early. Second, they caused the temperature of an evening cooled bedroom to rise to an uncomfortable level much too quickly, and third, if it was Wednesday, it was cleaning lady day.

Hating the light and heat, but too lazy to get out of bed, Lisa would pretend to be fast asleep when Lily, the cleaning lady came into her room to wake her up. She spoke a language that was enchanting but not quite English; a language that made Lisa hold onto each expression. As she was delicately shaken awake with Lily's rhythmical voice saying, "Good Mornin' good lookin' "Lisa would perform an academy award-winning performance of a flower awakening into bloom. It began with a few flutters of the eyelids, a yawn, and finally a smile for Lily, always in that sequence.

Lisa loved Lily. She was this "real" person who knew how dirty things were in their house. It mattered not at all how hard she needed to work as she dusted and mopped, carrying her basket of cleaning tools from room to room. Lily knew that Lisa's brothers would tear through the place several times undoing what she had just done. Lily didn't judge them. Lisa sometimes wondered what she must say to her husband Calvin after a day at the Palma's.

Lily Mathis could have taught a class on how to be a hired house servant. She was especially fond of the children in the house and if they did something like sneak the Whip-n-Chill bowl of instant chocolate pudding out of the refrigerator and eat it on the couch with a spoon, she never told Carla. If she found inappropriate reading material under the bed in the boys' bedroom, she would carefully move and stack the magazines so that the *Sports Illustrated* was on the top. She turned a blind eye to love notes folded several times in an intricate triangular shape, placing them in the top drawer of the desk in Marcy's room. Having Lily at their house was like striking gold. They all knew it and she knew it too.

There had been a bevy of hit-and-miss cleaning ladies that hadn't lasted long. Mrs. Fleming, in particular, was simply not equipped for the rambunctious nature of the family. She was not used to words delivered in shouts or the ease with which the children would mess up what she had just put right, without a care in the world.

Mrs. Fleming was a songwriter for her Baptist church choir. She was a very proper lady. It seemed as if the Palma's were beneath her just by their actions. It was hard to believe she cleaned houses for a living. It was like she had to take off her crown to come down to their level every other Wednesday, and put on her helmet.

One day, she told Lisa's fighting siblings to sit down in the living room. Marcy and Billy were shouting at each other at the tops of their lungs. Mom usually let flare ups like this burn out. They were usually territorial or involved food. Today was the former. Marcy was reading in the living room when Billy put his newest Rolling Stones album on the stereo console. The row escalated into an all-out war. When asking politely didn't work, and turning the volume down herself didn't work, Marcy did the logical thing and threw the LP record like a discus down the hall. Billy was aghast and didn't know what to do first, pick up the album or punch his sister in the face. He chose to pick up his album. In that time, Mrs. Fleming gave Carla Palma a withering look, and floated into the living room. Marcy and Billy squared off and an altercation was inevitable. But Mrs. Fleming was clearly not going to stand for this upheaval.

"I would like you to sit down in these chairs," she said calmly with a voice that lent itself to sovereign power. The tension in the room hissed out as if a leaking pinhole from a balloon. The kids looked at her, and she waited until their stunned faces registered that the cleaning lady was going to reprimand them. They sat down with arms folded. The body language saying to the sibling, this is only a *temporary* reprieve. They knew better than to rock this woman's boat, for if they did, Carla's unhappiness would be shared with Artie. His short temper could ignite. That could be another whole can of unwelcome worms.

Mrs. Fleming closed her eyes and took a breath.

"Do you children know what the Golden Rule is?" She asked quietly.

Marcy and Billy rolled their eyes. This woman was trying to be their boss? She was their hired lady! How dare she think about disciplining them! They waited for their mother to come in and intervene. They wanted to be saved from this lady and her stuffy ways. They could have duked it out and been done with it by now, already. This type of sitting still and listening was agony.

"Mom?" Billy called, "can you come here?"

But Mom had other ideas. She was listening from the next room. She was only too happy to let Mrs. Fleming have a stab at parenting. Perhaps she could get through to them where Carla could not.

"Well," Mrs. Fleming continued, "It is in the Bible. I will look it up for you. It's in the book of Matthew chapter 7, verse 12."

Billy yawned loudly. Marcy began to read the newspaper on the table.

"I would like your eyes to look and your ears to listen." Mrs. Fleming said.

"I would like a bologna sandwich with mustard and milk." Billy said.

Mrs. Fleming went silent. Not just for a moment. Actually Mom came rushing into the living room after three minutes had passed to make sure she hadn't fainted. But Mrs. Fleming hadn't done any such thing. She and Billy were having a staring contest, it seemed. She was willing Billy to learn his lesson and Billy was showing his insolent side. It was as if a silent ticker tape filled with worlds was being transferred between the two of them: Hateful. Proud. Bitch. Spoiled. Uppity. Lost.

"We are all listening. Please go on." Mom was now the mediator.

But Mrs. Fleming looked like a clipped bird.

"I would just like to say that you need to treat each other lovingly, not with anger. God is Love."

"Billy? Marcy?" Their mother looked at them. "Don't you have anything to say to Mrs. Fleming?"

Marcy quickly said no. But Billy said,

"Yes. Mrs. Fleming. You need to know your place and it is not in here telling me about Jesus."

All eyes swiveled to the defeated Mrs. Fleming. She should have known better. She turned and went into the first bedroom to clean, closing the door quietly.

"You two little spoiled bastards!" Their mother growled. "Just when someone works out to take a little of my load, you are going to ruin it for me! Wait until your father gets home!"

Billy and Marcy looked at each other when the adults had left the room. They laughed in giggles at first and then deep from their bellies. Such a convoluted scene! Their dad would certainly agree with them that the help should not be doing the parenting.

Lunch time on cleaning lady days meant everyone (adults and kids) sat down and ate lunch together at the table. Lisa's mother took all the children aside and told all the kids to have some good manners at the table today. Relieved that the twins were on a playdate and she really never had to worry about Lisa or Jane, her words were mainly for Marcy and Billy.

Grace was always said around the table, whether a cleaning lady was there or not. Lisa was especially anxious today. She knew her older brother tended to carry a grudge. She sensed danger for what might happen in the next 30 minutes.

She didn't have to wait long.

They bowed their heads to say the Catholic Grace. Its cadence went up and down with each group of words. Mrs. Fleming, not being of the faith, kept her head bowed and usually said a few words like "Peace on Earth." Or "Lord be praised" after amen was said. They all knew the words were coming at the end of their prayer. It made everyone smile at first when she added small prayer after grace. They knew there would be a phrase today. Lisa wondered if Mrs. Fleming could do it after the morning's events. But, Mrs. Fleming did not disappoint and she kept her eyes closed and opened her mouth to speak. But Billy beat her to the punch and interjected "God is love", his words dragged out like a preacher at a revival. Poor Mrs. Fleming was unable to get one word out. She snapped her mouth shut and continued to sit there with her eyes tightly shut. Lisa could see the muscles in her jaw, however. Clenching and unclenching, they seemed to be battling for control. The seconds ticked away until Billy caught Marcy's eyes. Unable to hold it in any longer, they busted out with laughter. Everyone else followed, that is, but Mrs. Fleming. Even Carla, who had tried so hard to be the guiding force today, had caved in to it. It felt light hearted, she thought until she watched Mrs. Fleming stand and mutter something about having lost her appetite.

Shock registered on Carla's face. She couldn't leave this group by themselves at the table right now. Each time she tried to begin on what was wrong with Billy's sassy behavior at the table, she started laughing. She sighed to herself that maybe she couldn't tame this wild bunch. She felt badly for their lack of respect for the cleaning lady, but was beginning to see Billy's side of things. She was the "cleaning lady." She was not the parent. Perhaps she had overstepped her boundaries.

Mrs. Fleming finished up and left two hours early. Mom went out to pay her and in exchange she was given a piece of paper. It was sheet music of a song Mrs. Fleming had written for her church.

"I am sure you know I will not be coming back." Mrs. Fleming told Lisa's mother, "But I will continue to pray for your bunch of hooligans because they are our future."

"I apologize for their behavior." Carla said, "If you need a reference, I would be happy to provide one."

Mrs. Fleming got into her old Buick. It had fins just like a fish, Lisa thought as she watched from the window.

Mother came back in with a determined look. She said,

"Well, I hope you all like chores, because Mrs. Fleming won't be coming back."

Lisa was not sure how this made her feel. To put a word on this type of ugly bad was difficult. They had all been rude to laugh. Why were those fits of laughter so hard to keep in?

She thought about when she laughed at the wrong time. She got the giggles in church sometimes. Especially at long Masses, where close observations could be made to deter from the ongoing monotone of the priest's homily. Something simple and unfunny would happen. It could be a noise or a gesture or a man's neck squeezed to overflowing the collar of a shirt that fit last year. The skin dripping over the sides and straining for the man to just please, undo the top button. Placing a pointing finger, laid atop an open palm, Lisa watched as Jane's shoulders began to shake. Convulsing herself, with tears streaming down her face, Lisa knew the object of this game was not to laugh out loud because that would lead to getting caught. But sometimes, no matter how many layers of stoicism had been used: pinching, biting the insides of the cheek, puckering lips, or putting the missal-ette in front of the face, weakness prevailed. It was Carla who knew that after the 15th minute of repetitive rhetoric, the kids would start acting up. At the ready, she leaned across and stepped in between the silliness in hopes of stemming the entire row from a break out. But Lisa would take her pointer and place it on her palm, and mother would look up at the red, bulging blob, and instantly tears fell freely down her own face as she desperately tried to gain her composure. Lisa really loved her mother at times like that. It was hard for her not to laugh along-side her children. She shared much of their joy.

Lisa knew what her mother knew. The boys would always be a handful. She had three of them, after all. But her husband Artie, would always hold up their behavior to be manly and not at all demeaning. They often used humor in their put downs and it got them out of many scrapes.

The treatment of Mrs. Fleming was no different. When Artie found out, he told Carla that the cleaning lady was there to clean. He wanted it made clear to her that discipline of the kids was not her job. He told Carla that the children should not be required to eat at the table on Wednesdays. But Carla violently opposed this. She wasn't going to sit and eat with the lady by herself! After all, it is what most people did on the block. The subject was sticky.

A full month passed after Mrs. Fleming's departure, before Lisa's mom found a new cleaning lady. But Lily had proven she could take the jokes. She laughed right along with the kids. The hazing started right away and Lily could not be more fun. She dished Billy out rip for rip until he was exhausted. Lily was everyone's simpatico. Lisa remembered thinking how considerate Lily had been to park on the street and come in through the garage. She even put her clothes in the pool shower room. It was nasty in there. Spider webs and old dried up bugs floated in the toilet water. It was supposed to be a place for people to shower before or after swimming in the pool, but no one really ever used it. It had become another place to store things like skis and old boots. How had Lily known that room was there? She wondered. Did someone tell her to use it? No, Lisa thought, she was like a member of the family. An auntie who came on Wednesdays to help her mom. Everyone talked and laughed with her. No one would have made her put her stuff in the garage on purpose.

Usually, Lisa and her five brothers and sisters ate lunch on the fly. A hastily made sandwich, or a spoon dipped into last night's leftovers, on the way to the beach, served nicely. But mom had stepped Wednesday lunches up so that all the kids would want to come to the table. Unlike Mrs. Fleming, there was never an argument to eat at the table on Lily Matthis' days. Mom made tuna fish or egg salad sandwiches cut on a diagonal and piled high on a plate. There was usually a big bowl of fruit, potato chips, pickles and always pudding. Mom cooked the pudding on her olive green, electric cooktop burners. The pudding was way better on chocolate days than vanilla days, because for some reason, she never failed to burn the bottom of the pudding pan and leave little black charred pieces that had everyone, including Lily, pawing around with their spoon to capture and put aside as discreetly as possible.

Poor mom. Cleaning lady days were harder on her than regular ones. The kids were told to pick up their rooms, a full day before Lily came, so she could get to the real dirt. But to Lisa, those were lucky days. With Lily there, grace was prayed as usual before lunch. Lily just bowed her head when she didn't know the words. She never said "God is love", and the group ate in their regular places around the table, with Lily in dad's spot and mom sitting across. Two bookend women. One black and one white. Both a little insecure but doing their best to hide it.

Sometimes, after lunch, Lisa would sneak upstairs to where Lily sat on her parents' bed and watched the soaps until they ended at 3:00PM. Lily always slowed down her cleaning when she got upstairs. She would pat a spot on the bed and quickly got Lisa caught up on what Bob and Nancy Hughes were up to in *As the World Turns*.

One day, while they watched soaps, Lisa's dad came home unexpectedly. Lily shot off the bed like a rocket, shooed Lisa downstairs, and picked up the duster like she was hard at work. Cool, Lisa thought. We have a little secret here.

Lily's husband, Calvin, worked in Chicago as a taxi driver.

He came home to Covert, a small town in Southwest Michigan, only on weekends.

Lily often regaled the kids at those round table lunches, of the events that occur in taxis that no one knows. Like the time a lady left a baby in his cab and Calvin was a good three blocks down Michigan Avenue when he heard a little peep from the back seat. There on the floor was a bundled up baby boy. It shook Calvin so much he had to pull over.

"You see," Lily said, "The baby was white!"

It was 1966 and he was a black cabbie with a bundled up white baby in his cab! He was starting to panic when dispatch radioed his cab and said the woman was at the main office and she was frantic. He told Lily that he left the baby in exactly the spot the mother had, because that would not sit well if he touched that baby to even move it. As it was, the mother had to be convinced that she had forgotten to pick the baby up with all her packages and such. That Calvin had not purposely driven away with it.

Lisa had mulled that story over for weeks afterward. She was uncomfortable with the questions that she was feeling. What if the baby couldn't breathe, would he have moved it then? What if the baby needed to eat? Would he have stopped somewhere for milk? She knew about hungry, crying babies. Barbara, her mom's friend, often brought her infant daughter over, and when she started crying it made Lisa head outside and far away from the house. Why wouldn't you calm the baby down by putting it right near you? Did Calvin not know how to hold a baby?

What was the problem there in the first place?

She asked Lily,

"Why didn't Calvin pick up that baby if it was crying?"

But as Lily began to answer mom said,

"Now, no more bothering Lily about her story. She has a lot to do upstairs this week."

And that was it.

At the time, most of the help at their house had been black. They weren't just women. Her dad found many jobs around the house that could have waited to be done, but knew people fell on hard times. There was Charlie, the odd jobs man who came over when he needed work. Dad would always find something for him to do. Whether it was staining a fence or painting the kitchen cupboards, he did anything he was given, happily. Everyone knew when Charlie was in the house. There was whistling and happy laughter. The mood was always light. He talked to her brothers about football a lot. At these times, Lisa felt like Dorothy in the Wizard of Oz movie when the servants beautified and freshened everyone up to see the Wizard. She liked the way she was called "Miss Lisa" instead of just Lisa. She felt like royalty.

When her father gave jobs to white men who were down on their luck, Lisa felt differently. They seemed mean and unhappy. They didn't sing or whistle like Charlie. They often seemed to have a chip on their shoulder and she heard them talk badly about her dad, even though he was giving them work. They seemed jealous almost. Sometimes they stood around lazily watching the other guys do all the work. They made remarks under their breath. One day, Artie even assembled the kids before a work crew came to build a new shed. He told them to stay away from the men that were coming to work.

"You kids stay out of the yard. And I mean it!"

He added that he didn't want them in the house, and the kids should tell him if they were. The men were to use the toilet in the garage and take their breaks under the tree.

Of course, this was both frightening and intriguing at the same time. Why were the men not allowed in the house? Were they ex-cons? With the pencils that hung straight down from the insides of their work hats and cigarettes pasted to their lips, they seemed extra dirty and a little mysterious. It was unsettling the way they got quiet when her sister Marcy walked the pitcher and glasses of lemonade out to the tree for their break. Marcy was the prime candidate to give them refreshments. She would never drop a glass from the tray, and if one person uttered an off color remark, she would conjure up the most withering look from her small, five foot body. The workers would become instantly quiet as all conversation died away. Her sister had perfected the Sister Jacinta look. JC, as they called the nun, stood at a microphone on a stage in the church basement during lunch time. She would stare first and then say the person's name who was getting demerits. Lisa wasn't sure who "Bernerd" was, but his name rolled off the nun's tongue over and over again.

Everyone on the block had some type of hired help over the course of the summer. It was mostly inside help and mostly black women. Sadie had Mary Rulet, who came every day. Mary wore an actual maid's costume. She had glasses and her smile was warm but not super friendly. She was the most professional of the bunch on Apache. Sometimes, Lisa reflected, Lily provided more companionship to her mother and it wasn't just about the cleaning. They had a "hidden" friendship. It was kind of like a Wednesday only friendship club. On other days of the week, it was not open.

Lisa wondered, if the opportunity came up would mom go to lunch with Lily. Would she have tea with her on her day off?

Sadly, she thought she probably knew the answer to that.

Lynn

Even though Lynn didn't live in the Zone, many of her friends and their families did. The community was a hive of honeybees. Buzzing, gyrating, and always in motion, it filled the gap of what they'd lost when they left Chicago. Living near Moon Park meant having their thumb on the pulse of the newest gossip. Lynn loved knowing and sharing news with her girlfriends. Who was together, whose husband had left, who was pregnant, who had lost their job were always the hot topics for the group of junior high school girls.

Mama found good work at an HR firm in an office downtown and remained the breadwinner. William's weekend work and side hustles could never pull down a steady salary. After Netti had been "let go" William could never seem to put in a full week's work. He began hanging around his "new boys" as he called them. They were big drinkers and most gravitated to hang out at William's house. He lived in an actual house with his wife and kids. They spent hours sitting in chairs at the garage entrance throwing back cheap wine and beer. An occasional joint or two was passed, but William lived in fear that Zenobia would find out and call it "Illegal mischief" and kick him out. He really had to beg after that whole Netti fiasco. It should have taught him a lesson to not mess with a drunk.

Close to town, Moon Park offered the best vantage point to watch the goings on in the area. Rain or shine the grills would be putting out the magic aromas of Cousin Johnny's barbeque smoker. The mouthwatering scent could wake a baby out of a sound sleep. Wafting into open car windows with basses turned up to a teeth rattling max, the promise of a bite or two caused some folks to pull over or double park to inquire what the occasion might be.

Lured like zombies to fresh meat, Cousin Johnny didn't have to have a reason to start his smoker. Sometimes it just felt like the time to have a party. He'd charge a reasonable price for a few forkfuls of pork that had been dragged through a tin of his signature sauce. Sometimes ladies around the neighborhood would contribute their own prize winning dishes. Macaroni and cheese or collard greens touched the very souls of those who brought their own plates and silverware to share the feast.

Food brought people together, Lynn thought. In times of lean and in times of plenty, her extended family contained all of the people who lived in and around the park.

Lynn often giggled to herself that people referred to the Zone as the "projects". She saw projects in Chicago. Those were more like concrete apartments around a common yard, built more in tune with a prison. The young teens are forced to sell drugs to help their families make ends meet. There was always trash around. Newspaper or used wrappers, carelessly dropped, littered the sidewalk and stuck up against chain-link fences as if they had planted. They had big crime in Chicago. It seemed like simple fist fights were turning into all-out-murders with guns. The lack of pride and the feeling of futility could not lift the Chicago projects. They seemed to be sinking into a hole.

It wasn't that there weren't good intentions for folks living in these projects. Many of the residents worked in labor jobs that were offered by the Department of Health and Human Services. Those lucky enough to work there would be trained to receive minimum wage salaries. Even if they were exemplary workers, they knew from watching others before them, that they would not be the ones to get a leg up. Often passed over for promotions and raises, they became angry. They felt as if they'd been thrown a "crumb" from the government. In fact, whenever an election was held, the new administration would reconfigure these jobs and that often meant layoffs. Who didn't want to do better by their family? Who didn't want to get what the American Dream was all about?

Mama said it was all about education. She pointed out that she went to college to get her associate's degree in accounting and was never at a lack for work. But public schools in the '70s were rat's nests. Federal money was not responsibly used. Getting into the very basic needs of the school communities was not consistently overseen. People knew it. As long as there was somewhere for their kids to go during the day, the quality of the educational programming was not given much scrutiny. And if it was, it took effort for almost every household to be present for the children. Tell that to someone with two babies and no job, Lynn thought.

Many single mothers in her neighborhood in Chicago, sensing their kids were going down a wrong road, would send them to aunties who lived in the Zone in the town of Heaven. Lynn was observant when someone new from the old "Block" came into town. At first, they would inquire about employment at the manufacturing jobs, but having to wait for openings or background checks or even the slowness of paperwork processing, soured them on the idea of working a regular job.

It was nearing 1971. The military problem in Vietnam and the disastrous Democratic Convention in Chicago had opened these young entrepreneurs to a rife and active drug trade. Learning in the streets of the big city, they brought drug merchandise and established a thriving business right inside the Zone. It was fat money. They liked working in the Park. It was an easy in and out to make an exchange of any size. Drugs had become a culture in small town America and a lucrative business for many dealers who set up shop there. Even white teens came into the Park. At first it looked as if they were coming to watch basketball, but after several minutes they left the bleachers without a backward look, and it became obvious that drugs were the motivation. It may have been called the projects to those who didn't know.

But the projects it was not. Not to Lynn.

To her, the homes with a front and back yard, poured concrete parking space, and sometimes a small concrete pad patio represented an orderliness that she hadn't had in Chicago. This was a place where neighbors were very much the same.

Community, worship, school, and employment located in a neat and tidy four block radius.

There were five churches within the four corners. The park, in the center, was a year-round gathering place. It was a nightly display of basketball prowess in the summer. In the winter, the snow shovels came out and, as long as the snow wasn't accumulating, could be a winter basketball showcase as well.

When they first moved into town, Lynn felt that she could walk the seven blocks to downtown with ease. But that only meant physically. There was an unseen dividing line, however invisible, that was difficult to cross. It was about three blocks from the Zone. Only white families lived in those places. If you were black, walking from the Zone to town might be a little more of a zigzag than a straight route.

Lynn remembered her first walking trip downtown. She and her new friend, Diann were walking to the little Superette on the corner on the main drag, close to the river. When they were passing a beautiful garden filled with flowers, Lynn remarked to a white woman weeding that she had done a beautiful job on her garden. The woman looked up with a smile, but when she saw Lynn and Diann, her mouth gradually unplugged itself, like a clock that had run out of power. The girls stopped, confused by the reaction to Lynn's compliment.

"Keep moving," a man said as he came around the corner of the garage. "She knows what it looks like."

Lynn stood a moment longer staring at the man. She was shocked by his tone and lack of manners. She began to say something about it, but Diann nudged her along.

"Just go," she said.

It wasn't until they crossed the next street that Lynn turned to Diann and said,

"Girl. That man was rude. Why can't I tell him how I feel?"

"Because, Lynn, this isn't Chicago. People around here tolerate us if we stay in our area, but they don't, for a minute, want you to think they want to be friends."

"That just doesn't make sense, Diann. I didn't want to be that lady's friend! I just wanted to give her a compliment."

"Here's the big picture, Lynn. You are better off to walk straight ahead and not be noticed. For that couple in their yard, up in your face, there are probably ten others looking at what we're doing from their windows. We don't belong on their street. It is a pass through."

"Well, that is just messed up." Lynn said,

"It is but it's better you know this now." Diann said,. "Heaven may seem like a small town to you, but there are some pretty old school types that don't think we should even have the Zone within the city limits, and they are the ones who built it!"

Lynn was quiet the rest of the way to the store. When they got there, she picked through her items and put them on the counter. An extremely friendly Italian man smiled at her.

"Did you get everything you need?" he asked

"Yes. Sir. Thank you."

The man looked at her somber face. He said, "I believe you have forgotten something."

"Huh?" Lynn said.

"You forgot to put a smile in your basket! We sell them for

free!' He pulled a little yellow smiley face button out of a basket. "I hope it brightens your day."

Lynn thanked the man, and she and Diann started the walk home.

"Okay. So how should I have approached that man?" she asked Diann.

"Lynn. You will figure out who you can have a conversation with and who you can't. Not all white people are going to be rude. But he was a businessman, not a homeowner. There are all different levels."

"This is too much to think about. Just get me home." Lynn said.

Back at the Park, droves of men just released from their factory shifts were ambling tiredly by. The park was right in the middle of the Zone and the men passed by on their way home. Their day had begun at 7:00 AM. with a whistle and ended at 3:30 PM. Four whistles blew in unison two times a day. No one needed to ask the time, they would just say, "have the whistles blown yet?"

Many of the men were covered with grease or oil from working on pianos, or car motors, or picture frames. The old wood products factory that skirted the railroad tracks had closed. In years past, the freight train would be filled up at the loading docks there to carry products to faraway places. But, these days, with the efficiency of highways, it was much easier to fill a truck at the plant and send it from there. It cut a full three days to a week off delivery time.

Many factory workers eased into the bleacher seats at the

park for a quick break on their way home. Friends handed them paper bags and they took long pulls from MD 2020 or Muscatel. But most of the men chit chatted along the way eager to get home to families and dinner. The unwinding could be a Cubs game on television or smoking on the picnic table out back. Later, rejuvenated, they might return to the park to watch up and coming young basketball stars perform.

Walking into the park after dinner was something Lynn loved to do with her friends. She and the rest of the girls loved watching the boys play ball. Sometimes they hung out on picnic tables, flirting and cutting up. Lynn loved this time of her teens innocently feeling the center of attention, with her widest grins always showing off her straight white teeth. Both she and her girlfriend Diann, would get all dolled up to make an impression on the young men who were looking. They each had their eyes on a few of the guys who played basketball. The girls elbowed each other when the shirts came off during a game. It was typical for boy crazy preteens, and they sat and cheered for basketball league games or participated in some softball games. Mostly, they stuck around afterward for a lot of loud laughter and back smacking conversation, but never were out past the street light curfew.

Lynn's mother, Zenobia wore the pants in the disciplining of her children. They went to church every Sunday. They ate real meals. It was not just the awful things her friends gave their children from the government food source. Although much of the cooking was done by Lynn, the ingredients were there to put together meals full of flavor and nutrition. Zenobia was the breadwinner, wise council, matriarch and confidante. She wanted the best for her children.

As Lynn approached high school, Zenobia noticed Lynn's sudden attraction to wearing makeup and tight clothes. Knowing full well she was going to keep a close eye on her daughter and her friends, Zenobia often used the eyes of other mothers in the community, and they hers, to trace the daughters' movements throughout the day and many evenings.

One day, long after supper on a summer evening, Zenobia was enjoying her favorite drink, Mogan David Cream Sherry with her best friend Louise in the kitchen. She heard Lynn and her girlfriends' loud giggling and talking in the bedroom upstairs. She told her friend:

"My daughter is going to try and put one over on me tonight."

Her friend smiled and said,

"If I know you, Zenobia, she'll be learning a new lesson tonight."

They laughed quietly. "You don't get to this age without being around the block a few times."

Lynn and her friend Diann burst into the kitchen.

"Good Lord, Lynn!" Her mother exclaimed. "Did you pour that perfume all over yourself? Where did you get that halter top? And may I ask who gave you those high heeled shoes?"

"Mama!" Lynn said breathlessly, "I am dressed to go to a party. It is at the park. But we will be home when the street lights come on. So like 11:00 PM?"

Zenobia noticed that four more girls joined Lynn and Diann. She looked carefully at each one, making sure she knew their names. She said to the group,

"I need some help finding my reading glasses. Girls, please run upstairs and look for me. Oh, and

please make sure the beds are made."

With the footsteps on the stairs, she went around the corner to the phone. She had just returned to her seat when Diann came running down the stairs with the reading glasses.

"I found your reading glasses, Ms. Zenobia," Diann said quickly.

Lynn and the five girls clunked down the stairs like a herd of elephants.

Breathlessly, Lynn exclaimed, "We're heading out then." She looked at the group behind her, so far so good, her eyes sparkled with glee.

"Now, what were you talking about, Lynn?" Zenobia said slowly.

"We are heading to the park. But now, it's a little later than we thought we were going to be, so can we come back about half an hour later?"

"Hmm." Her mother said low and deep. "So there's a party at someone's house near the park? Or is it at the park?"

"It's at a house, Mama. You're being silly." Lynn sidled up to her mother.

"I hope it's someone new," her mother said, "because I have told you that you will not be going to any party given by Patrice Winslow. Is this Patrice's party you are trying to get to?"

The wheels were turning inside of Lynn's head. She knew if her mother caught her in a lie it would be worse. She really hoped she could leave out that Patrice part.

"It's at Patrice's house, but I don't think she is the one actually giving the party." Lynn said slowly, feeling like she was being buried alive.

"Is that right?" Her mother said, looking almost joyful. Louise's eyes were crinkling in the corners. Lynn knew she had to think of a plan B. "In that case the answer is still no."

"What do you mean? She may not even be there. Everyone else is going. " Lynn said, the sinking feeling deepening. She knows too much. We have to go to plan B, she thought.

"Well, if you recall, I told you that you didn't need to be going to any of those parties, no matter the host. They are unsupervised. I have always told you to bring your friends here. Plus, haven't I already said no?"

"Okay, Mama." Lynn said a little too quickly. "We will just walk the others home." This was Plan B. Anything to get out of the house.

Zenobia looked at her friend Louise, time for the kill move.

"No need. When you went upstairs to look for my glasses, I called all your mothers. They have given permission for you to spend the night here, at this house. So no one is leaving."

Lynn looked at her friends. Her eyes seemed to say, "she's too slick for me, dammit." But she didn't utter a word. She looked at her friends.

"Want to play cards?"

Lisa

She was stuck again. Even though her father had a Cadillac as his company car, smooshing her family of eight in there for the biannual trip to grandpa's in the South Chicago suburbs was always met with tough whining and fighting. Jane was up front between her mom and dad. That was just the way it was. No one got mad at the little one. Jane was Lisa's special baby sister. But the back seat often made for quick tempers. Even if Lisa had called "Shot Gun" she would not have gotten a window seat. Usually Marcy and Billy, her older brother and sister would take the window and that would stick her next to Tim and Tommy, the twins. No seat was roomy enough for six kids.

Lisa knew better than to even touch clothes with them. She knew the twins fought as a team, and it was never fair. Why, when she had her ears pierced at the doctor for her nine-year-old birthday, the twins chased her to the bathroom where they cornered her in the tub. Tim had the lead while Tommy watched out for mom. He was angry that she turned their favorite cartoons off. He and Tommy were thinking of how to make her pay. They chose the earrings, of which she was so proud. Tim reached out and grabbed the dangling purple earring and tugged with all his might.

The pain was excruciating. She screamed so loudly that her mother came running. The twins were caught and they proceeded to wail. They were such fakers but everyone adored them. It didn't work this time for when her mom checked her ear, she took a sharp intake of air. The piercing had surprisingly little blood, but the hole itself was a long, jagged affair. Mother called her dad at work. He came home and spanked the boys and sent them to their rooms, then drove Lisa to the Doctor's office where the earrings were removed. As she silently wept over the loss of the earrings and the fact that the doctor said they must grow in and maybe she could try again next year, she knew that could never happen. The twins had won. Even receiving a spanking was not a punishment for them. It was just a collateral means to an end. Their smug smiles burned into her brain.

No, she really was stuck with them for now. She must choose the lesser of the two older evils when planning the sitting position for the next few hours. She chose to sit next to Marcy. She brought her 3 ring notebook to put up as a barrier to Tommy. She concentrated on keeping her space in the back seat until they reached her grandpa's tailor shop in the Hills (a south suburb of Chicago). The trip was two and a half hours, with no stops. It made her back ache and joints hurt to stay immobile for that long.

Her cousins lived a big city life. Although not luxurious, they had access to stores like Korvette's. It was a huge department store playground of products found on real television ads, with wide aisles of games and toys, or clothes. A person could spend a whole day in the store. A place where Auntie Raina would take the girls only, making the hardship of the drive worthwhile.

Of course, the food on these trips was always delicious. Lisa's aunties strove to make all the specialty Italian dishes when the family got together. On their trips, the family would split up. The boys and Marcy liked to stay with cousins, but that would mean mother had to stay there too. Dad would stay with whomever was left at his father's house. That was usually Lisa and Jane. The uncles (her dad's brothers) would stop in, and Lisa would read to Jane and generally play with her until the entire family joined up again.

Grandpa Palma's home was in the Hollow Hill neighborhood. It was an area where there were Italian names on businesses. The Catholic Church and school that her father attended as a small boy was still in operation. There was a railroad line that went behind grandpa's house where trains, loaded with gravel and rocks would chug along, whistles blowing into the night.

Lisa visited grandpa many times. He was a tailor and the first stop on these car trips was to his tailor shop. It was always the same. He would be listening to his radio placed high on a shelf. Italian opera music or a baseball game would be turned up loudly. There was no grandma. She died when Lisa's father was 12. Diabetes and a thyroid problem, she thought. No one really discussed her since it had been decades and Grandpa P. never remarried.

This visit, they pulled up into the alley behind Palma and Sons tailor shop. Uncle Shiny was just getting out of his cleaners delivery truck and hugged his brother. He was a smiley one. Lisa liked him at a distance. But he liked to shout when he'd had too much to drink, and she really didn't like this side of any of the brothers. They were noisy.

Walking into the tailor shop, her grandfather would look up with a smile. Each kid was kissed, cheeks pinched and sometimes slapped, and questioned about their health as they inhaled the cigar smoke that was rising up from the soggy end of the stogie left burning in the ashtray. It had been a hot ride. Lisa asked her mother for a glass of water. Her mom said to wait. Lisa turned to point out the sink behind her but stopped herself. The tap and handles were covered with a crystalized white substance like she saw in pictures of caves. Later, she learned that it was limestone. The mineral would stay on the leaky faucet long after the water had evaporated. It would take a chisel to get through the three inch buildup. Never mind, she thought. Her thirst had left her. She would get to grandpa's house before having a drink. Even then, the mineral filled water was harshly different than the Lake Michigan water that came out of her tap at home.

Uncle Mario came in from the front of the store.

"You are all invited to come see the new house tonight!" He said proudly. Lisa didn't know exactly what Uncle Mario did, but she thought it had something to do with the cleaners and the tailor shop. She rejoiced, hoping they would sleep there too. She heard the new house had an indoor pool, and that there was wall-to-wall carpeting throughout. She loved her Auntie Julie, Mario's wife. She looked like a movie star most of the time, except in the morning before she put her makeup on. It was a breathtaking transformation when seen from beginning to end.

After they left the tailor shop, with the house key, her father stopped at the Dorticelli's Deli across the street from grandpa's house on the 'Hill'. There he bought loaves of fresh Italian bread, crusty hard on the outside and soft and cottony inside. Her mouth watered at the feast that they would have for lunch at grandpa's. Sandwiches of salami, capicola, mortadella, and provolone would be up for grabs! Jars of hot and spicy giardiniera in olive oil could be slathered on for a condiment. The family would hover around the table as her father undid the sheets of white paper. They would 'ooh and ahh' as each deli treat was uncovered. Dad would be extra dramatic in his pronunciation of each meat or cheese:

" Mor-ta-dell-ah! Pro-shute-o! Cap-i-cola! ..." he would announce as he cut the last syllable to a halt.

It was as if he was revealing a very special secret surprise. The family knew it was as special as something made of gold. These flavors could never be found in Heaven. The plastic stacked, Eckrich Hard Salami sold at the tiny, corner grocery was the closest they got to the time-cured meats of a real Italian deli.

Perhaps the greatest thing about this meal was the bottle of Pepsi Cola each of the kids was given; just to drink for themselves. No sharing with brothers and sisters. Backwash was only your own. It was something that didn't happen anywhere else. This made the two-and- a-half hour drive worth it. Lisa's parents were very strict about drinking pop. They were allowed one small glass of Coke on Friday nights, with some popcorn. That was it. During the week, they drank white milk delivered by the Heavenly Dairy milkman.

But the heft of holding a full bottle of Pepsi Cola was like lifting a barbell in a weightlifting championship. The bottles had a way of feeling more substantial than having the bubbling brown goodness poured out in a glass, somehow. The frosted bottles dripped with magical cooled dew that covered fingers with moisture and required concentration so as not to let the bottle slip out of one's hands. Lisa had to slow down her sipping or she would be disappointed that her long tugs on the bottle would not quench her thirst.

It made the dreary kitchen, with its little window that looked out on the tracks and the plastic covered furniture in the adjoining room, seem a bit less alien. For Lisa, it was a fearful place. There was not one touch of a woman in the house. The "furnishings" were not warm. Everything was strictly utility. That, combined with the news stories from the nearby city of Chicago, of murdered nurses, civil unrest, mobsters; grandpa's swirling cigar smoke, and the way that no one spoke words here but shouted them, made her stomach hurt. It was familiar yet hostile. It made her both clingy and withdrawn. Everyone had cousins that were near their ages and they usually paired up and went off to play. Lisa really didn't have a cousin like that. She found herself reading and doing homework, squirreling away in the small bedroom inside of grandpa's house.

Now, much to her chagrin, Lisa noted that her Uncle Remo had been staying in the small bedroom within a bedroom, in the house. The room was an oddity she rather liked about this row house. It added a layer of safety from the outside alley. Grandpa's room had a door. To get to the small bedroom, one had to go through his room. Maybe robbers and murderers would think twice before breaking into a room inside a room. It would probably make them feel trapped. Her uncle's presence was noted not with anything out of place, but with two or three "Chicago True Crime" magazines on the nightstand. She knew now, she would never sleep. They drew her to them like a magnet. Thumbing through them, she peeked with one eye to see photos of murdered mobsters littering the pages. Why would anyone want to have this around as reading material?

Lisa's father was a reader of good, thick books. His books were often written by popular bestselling authors and were a sure thing in the gift department on Father's Days and birthdays. She appreciated that about him. She loved watching him on the couch, reading glasses askew, buried in a story. He was a very well read man, yet, sometimes he would pretend that he wasn't. Especially when visiting his home in the Hills. Most of his old friends and family did not get the chance to go to college. They stayed behind in family businesses or became tradesmen in their own right. It was as if he didn't want to look educated in front of them. Often, he changed to be like he was before as a kid, their youngest brother.

He never wanted them to think he felt better than they were. He always wanted to fit it with his group, never wanted to seem like he was a "college boy" or some sort of egghead. After all, he only got the chance at college because of an athletic scholarship. While at school, he worked hard at low paying jobs to earn money for food and shelter. It had always been a familiar struggle for him to put food on his table. He was a fantastic provider and not once did any of his children feel they wouldn't be fed or taken care of. He taught his children the value of saving money. But he could never put a price on his pride when it came to his family. Although there were six children, each one of them received a personal letter when he went on the annual Men's Retreat at church. No college education could have bought this sense of family for him. He knew it and was determined to preserve it.

Because they mostly visited the 'Hill' in late spring or early fall, the house was always hot. There were no fans. Opening windows meant becoming a continuation of the house on either side. Houses with windows so close, you could practically crawl through to the next house if the window was open. Aromas from kitchens, loud Italian words, crying babies all seemed to be taking place right in your living room.

It made Lisa so glad she didn't live here all the time. The water tasted funny and the air had a smell like when a hard-boiled egg was peeled. Everything moved fast. She could not get over the gray and black of living in a larger city. It was as if the beauty of her life, with its sunsets over Lake Michigan, the lush trees and farmlands, faded to gray the minute they crossed the Indiana State Line. As she grew older, Lisa realized that her cousins were not that different from her. As she approached her teens, she actually didn't mind learning more about herself as second generation Italian. Her dad always joked he was an F.B.I., and the rest of us kids were only H.B.I., since our mother wasn't Italian at all.

Although she was not a 'Full Blooded Italian" everything

about Lisa identified with the culture's dominant genes in physical traits. Her looks were definitely more like her father's: short, stubby legs, fat sausage fingers, and dark almond shaped eyes. Her nose, thankfully, was smaller due to a genetic piece broken off from her mother's side. Lisa and her siblings called their cleft chins "Butt chins." Her carriage and attitude was one of: *"Take no shit, because you are the shit."*

This was a learned trait though and not an inherent trait.

Playing with cousins and eating heaps of angel hair pasta with homemade meatballs and sausage was a highlight of these family gatherings. Cheeks smeared with sauce and peals of laughter were two things that made Lisa glad for her heritage. What she didn't love were the endless bottles of wine being consumed by her dad and the uncles. Her mother would pass through every now and then reminding her father he needed to drive home in a few hours. In other words, "Sober the hell up." But one thing led to another and soon the hot headed brothers were at each other's throats for some past sin. Tempers flared. Voices shouted words like "Mama Luke" and "Ma Donn." With each rising crescendo Grandpa P.,got more and more quiet. It was like watching a rubber band winding up. But as with all potential energy, there is a conversion to kinetic moving energy. For when Grandpa had enough, he stood up and out-yelled all of them. It was a lesson in power. That little man could harness the nastiest of fights into one bundle and throw it away. When he spoke, all the brothers quieted.

When it was time to leave the Hill, there was a sense of relief. They had two and a half hours ahead in the tight, hot car, but it would be quiet. Sometimes they would go visit right between Thanksgiving and Christmas. The drive around Lake Michigan was often a ride through blinding snow with flakes as large as baseballs. The snowfall mesmerized the riders and many times Lisa's mother would hint to her husband that he needed to move to the right or center as she navigated him through the highway, mile after mile, until he pulled safely into the driveway.

Lynn

The air was so wet it created a slimy sheen on lawn chairs and blades of grass. Lynn watched the outside of her glass erupt into water droplets as soon as her grandmother poured in the cold juice.

"What's on your mind, Sugar Plum?" her grandmother asked as she heard Lynn sigh for the third time that morning.

'It's too hot to do anything." Lynn replied, "I feel like a wet noodle."

"Oh honey, it is warm today," her grandma said, "Why don't we see about a trip to the beach this afternoon?"

 Lynn brightened up.

"Yes! Can I ask a friend?"

"Anyone but that mean Shirley Bell. I don't ever want the likes of her around you. I saw her the other day practically sitting on top of James Will. No one ever watches her. She will be..." Grandmother was on a roll. Lynn would ask her friend Diann. They were close and she didn't have to go a long way to meet her.

It was a process to get ready to go less than two miles to the South Beach. Grandmother insisted on having food on hand for snacks. The little concession stand was very expensive. Although she would put some sweet treats in the cooler, the children would have to use their own money to buy treats from the store. When the cooler was packed, it was time to pack the car. They used regular sized bath towels. Beach towels were coming into vogue, but one had to be practical on how much you were willing to spend on a piece of cloth to take to the beach. They would spread out the old bedspread and everyone would fit on it. Grandma always brought the plastic chair woven with a blue and white pattern. She found it along the side of the road. It had one strip of plastic missing so she wove in some of her old rags to make a sturdier seat than ever.

Lugging the things to the car, Grandmother told Lynn they would have five in total. Her sister had a friend and she had counted herself. All girls! The rules were given once inside the hot car. No one goes out of sight of Grandmother. If they do, they will spend the day on the sand. Also, set up will be right near the lifeguard stand.

By the time she was finished, they had pulled into a parking place at the South Beach. It was early in the day, so there were many places to choose from. The sand was not very hot at the moment. Flip flops were on just in case. Everyone was given an armful to carry.

Grandmother was thinking how much she loved to share Lake Michigan with her grandchildren. The free beach, sparsely crowded at this time of day, was one of their small wonders. Sure, this beach was located by the water filtration plant and was often looked down upon by visitors, who chose the sugary expanse of the north side beach, but they didn't know what Grandmother knew. Her children had a higher chance of being saved if this water got wavy. The flag color was green, which meant it was calm, but she had seen it roil up in the matter of minutes when the wind picked up from the north. On the north side of the river, the beach extended for at least two city blocks. The south beach was her favorite because it was about half a block and very compact.

They waved to Ron the lifeguard. He smiled and waved. The zinc oxide triangle on his nose made him appear like the scarecrow in the Wizard of Oz. The girls took turns running in and out of the waves. They were not good swimmers. Even though the high school had a pool and offered lessons in the summer, the kids they knew didn't like to have to be in water over their heads and the lessons cost money. Most of the time they stayed in their neighborhoods just running through the sprinkler. The need to swim was mostly for days like these when cooling off was a necessity.

Lynn and Diann were splashing water at each other in a frenzy of laughter, when an older woman passed them. Her bathing suit was doing everything in its power to hang on, even though the seams were screaming to be opened like a prisoner wanting out. Her pale, white legs had broken, purple veins interwoven within the stretch marks. The backs of her arms dangled and swayed as she walked.

"You girls know you shouldn't be at the beach until after 5:00 PM", she said with a dark look. "This town has an understanding."

All the laughter drained from the faces of the girls.

"I don't know what you mean?" Lynn said. "It opens at 9:00 a.m."

"Not for the colored." The woman hissed.

The girls were looking at each other with surprise. But the woman was menacing. They stood frozen in their steps.

Lynn's grandmother watched the exchange. She could tell it wasn't pleasant as soon as the woman thundered into the water, like she was a hungry hippo on a mission to find some prey.

"Lynn! Diann!" she shouted. "I have lunch ready for you. Please clean up and come make a plate."

Even though Grandmother had been talking to the girls, she never took her eyes off the big woman in the water. Inside was a familiar rage. If she responded to the woman, most likely an ugly exchange would ensue. She decided to take the high road, again. Oh, she would let it out when she discussed it with her friends, but she did not want her granddaughter to see her lose her cool.

"Grandma! Did you hear what that lady told us? Is that true?" Lynn was stricken. She had felt and heard rebuffs before but nothing directly addressing her. She felt afraid. She felt like she had broken the rules even though they weren't listed anywhere.

"Baby Girl," Grandma said, "Those are NOT the rules and you know that."

"But why did that lady say it was?"

"Girls, there are some things that people learn when they are young that are just plain wrong." Grandmother said, "We need to pray for that woman with all our strength."

"Pray for her?" Lynn exclaimed "I'm about to mess her up. Why I should…"

Her grandma cut off.

"Yes, pray for her because that bathing suit is going to give up the fight and release what it's holding in. And that poor, white whale is going to be naked for all to see!"

The girls let go with peals of laughter. Even Ron, the life-guard, overheard her, and was chuckling.

"I hope that doesn't happen." He leaned over to the group from his perch on the lifeguard stand. "Because then I will have to go in there and save her."

Even though they had salvaged the day and managed to have the best lunch of grandma's cold fried chicken and potato salad, they all were quieter than when they first arrived. They kept an eye on the lady in the blue suit as she opened her greasy bag of potato chips and drank her Mountain Dew from a bottle. They watched her as she smoked cigarette after cigarette, putting the butts in the sand when she was done. Her skin was turning a bright shade of pink as they began packing up their beach things. She had made them wary. Grandmother hated the lesson they were being taught.

As they marched through the growing beach crowd, Grandma feigned a stumble and a load of dry sand landed smack dab next to the junk food sated woman splayed on her beach blanket. The snoring was so loud, her transistor radio blaring out the top 40 hits could not compete.

Lynn's grandmother was still smoldering when she got to the car.

"I have one thing to say to you girls." She said, "Don't ever let another person tell you that you have different rules than they do. Times are changing. People of color have every right to go to the beach, join clubs, enter into contests and sports, and be proud of their heritage. That is why we call it Black Pride. We are proud to have overcome our obstacles and even when some white lady, who can't control her appetite, tells you differently, you need to believe in how you were raised. You are classy and kind. And that is all I am going to say on the matter."

Lisa

Apache Court had beach parties for all the families that lived there. The parents seemed to all be about the same age and loved to congregate at the end of the day before dinner in the street. There were a couple parties a year. The steep lake bank presented problems for getting food and drink down to the strip of sand. The smoothest spot on the bank was sited first. Then a sort of sledding run was started in the sand. Tables, cases of beer and pop, coolers, and indestructible food containers were sent first. Dads were posted at the top, middle, and bottom to keep things moving.

Once, after a few drinks, Mr. Becker decided to roll the watermelons down the bluff. It was a comedy to watch as the watermelon lofted into the air and Artie skillfully caught it, just like a football. The whole group was cracking up until they realized that Mr. Becker was sending two at a time and Artie hadn't handed off the watermelon he was holding. Crack! The melons split in two and covered Artie with guts.

On regular evenings parents milled around in the street awaiting the sunset. Most parents drank mixed drinks. There wasn't one divorced parent, although there were many couples that openly argued. The group was a homogenous makeup of white, European descent either second or third generation. Within that grouping, sub groups could be divided by churches: Catholic, Congregational, Methodist, Hebrew, or Agnostic. Although they would all be lumped into the "middle class" label, many of them seriously did not know what the others were worth. Even though the kids all played together on the street and at the beach, there were still profound differences.

One was the signal for dinner. Every family had an original 'come in for dinner' call.

There was the bell-ring for Sadie's call.

"Boys!" The Becker boys' call from their father.

"Linda, Ronnie. YaHA" This was Mrs. DeJoon's call. She was from the Netherlands.

"Palma's come eat!" Marcy only had to yell it once. Sometimes she merely stood on the bluff to yell to the kids on the sand below. There were arguments that it might be possible to hear Marcy from two towns over.

Another difference was the degree of parenting that went on. Some moms and dads stayed on the bluff long after sunset. They became louder as the pitchers of mixed Island drink favorites were refreshed. Often, the kids that attended Catholic School had the strictest rules. The Palma kids went in with the street lights, no matter what. Begging for at least a chance to finish the Kick the Can game, could bring serious repercussions. Baths and bedtimes for them were observed throughout the year. Others were not checked at all. Some parents felt that if they were in the boundaries of the dead end street, nothing could go wrong.

It made Lisa angry to watch them still playing outside well after she'd had a bath and was in her nightgown. Sometimes Sadie would come to her window and they would talk strategy.

Lisa loved those long late evenings when parents, with leather bound glass holders, strolled together. With the later nights, the walks were often cocktail parties on the lawns of those living right on the water. Since sunset didn't arrive until after 10:30 PM the group stayed until the wee hours of the morning. It was an excuse for them to unwind and allow the kids to move in a pack so supervision would not be required. The kids looked after themselves with neighborhood games of "Kick the Can" or "Mother, may I?" The only light that mattered was the streetlights.

Often the topic of conversation turned to the two men who lived in the cottage directly behind Lisa's house. Bob Mannert was a hairdresser. He owned a little poodle named "Pierre Beauregard." Pierre Beauregard was never called just Pierre. He wore a different bow every day in his white poodle hair. Bob painted his nails to match the bow. Everyone enjoyed Bob's company. During the week, he came alone to the happy hours on the neighborhood lawns. His salon was located up near Saugatuck, although he gave the neighborhood kids haircuts every now and then.

Once Lisa was receiving a haircut, while perched on a kitchen stool, in her home. Sitting still, so Bob could cut and talk, she would find herself drawn to his bright clothes and daring hue of pink and lavender ascot ties. He told some pretty dirty jokes and Carla would look over at Lisa as if to say, "Oops."

Why would her mother give him a "pass" when he said naughty words? Still, all the neighborhood seemed to gravitate toward him and he kept the parents in stitches.

The other man who lived there on weekends was Joe. He was not outgoing and would prefer to stay away from the grownups. Joe Shanor was the most handsome of the pair. Girls swooned over him and wished they could see him more often. He was dark and aloof. His drink of choice: sparkling water. He sunbathed on the beach by himself and developed a gorgeous tan. Lisa thought of Johnny Weissmuller from Saturday morning TV, or a model from body builders in magazines. His muscular shoulders and chest tapered down to a tiny waist. Upper legs were like frog legs if they were stretched out, really bulgy on top and tight as rubber bands. It was a mystery as to why Joe didn't have a girlfriend. Weirdly, none of the ladies in the neighborhood tried to set him up with sisters of friends. It seemed like the kids were all missing the main clue.

Joe was a kid loving kind of guy. He brought fun along every Saturday. New toys, called Frisbees, whizzed around the Ellis' yard that summer. Joe worked as an inventor in Grand Rapids. Mostly his products were prototypes, and the Apache Court kids were the first to see them and were all being used as guinea pigs. When he brought the pointed lawn darts for the kids to try out, he had no idea how sharp the actual metal ends would be as they traveled through the air to land inside the circle of plastic. Billy and Doug Becker got into a tussle over whose turn it was. While gesturing with the lawn dart, Billy gashed Doug in the forehead. Joe immediately removed the game. He went door to door apologizing to the parents. What a disaster. It ended all the new fun stuff for a while.

Joe felt awful for the kids. Billy and Doug finally made up and things were going back to normal. On a particularly wavy day with red, "No Swimming" flags posted at the public beaches, Joe asked the moms if he could take a group of neighborhood kids out on his super-duper new raft. Three or four mothers were meeting in the side yard between Palma's and Ellis's. Lost in the town gossip and smoking, the women got silent when Joe approached. Lisa thought they must be tongue tied because Joe was looking extra dreamy today with his muscles bulging out of his poor boy shirt. The women searched each other's eyes at his swimming inquiry and finally, Shirley, the oldest and most in charge, gave her permission and the rest of the group gave theirs too.

Her mother leaned down to Lisa and said, "stay close to your brother."

As if.

Lisa thought I am sticking by the strongest guy there. She watched as Joe brought the huge raft down the lake bank steps. It wasn't a blow up raft like the kids were used to. It was rolled up tightly like a carpet. When unrolled it was placed in the water on the sandbar so that everyone could jump on. Lisa worked her way over to Joe.

"Jump on! He yelled over the roar of the waves. But still Lisa waited for Joe to get situated.

She knew he was a strong swimmer. He pulled her onto the raft and jumped on himself, belly first.

Oh! What a day that had been!

Pummeled by wave after wave, the hefty raft held them all. Joe had them all hold hands across the raft and she made sure it was Joe's hand she had. The kids knew better than to go in Red Flag water. They would have never tried this by themselves. But with Joe, they felt invincible. He was the strongest and most capable man they knew and he was no stranger to the water.

He swam every morning he was in town. The word was, he had been a Navy Seal. Lisa knew just when to look out at him from the upstairs balcony of her parent's bedroom. He wore a Euro style bathing suit and brought a big towel but never used it. He often swam 30 laps back and forth in front of their bluff. Bob would sometimes appear to watch. In a white, fuzzy robe and puffing a cigarette, he stood looking at Joe from above. He talked as if in deep conversation to Pierre Beauregard about Joe but the stuff he said didn't make sense.

"He must think I am getting fat, Pierre Beauregard." He'd say. "I am afraid this one won't be around much longer."

It made Lisa sad and she wasn't sure why. Was Joe sick? Was it Bob? Maybe Joe had to move. She would ask her mother when she thought about it.

But she never had a chance because a few weeks later, Bob came over to speak to her mother and he had been crying. Her mother put her hand on his shoulder as if to console him. When Artie arrived home, Bob scurried back to his cottage behind the house. Mom never said anything to her husband about Bob's sad day.

Later that day, though, it was her mother's turn to host the neighbor ladies for bridge. Bob was the hottest topic since Jeannie Berman got pregnant a few years ago.

"Poor. Bob." Carla said to the ladies at the two tables. "I think he really loved Joe," she said. Huh? Lisa thought I loved him too.

Lisa busted into the living room. The cigarette smoke was so thick she had to squint to find her mother.

"Mom?" She said breathlessly, "Did Joe die?"

A few women tittered. But most were watching her mom, who looked stricken. She said

"There is nothing wrong with Joe. He's fine." And then she quickly interjected: "He had to move away for a job."

It was as if someone had plugged the group back in. Lisa looked around. Did E.F. Hutton just finish talking? The ladies seemed to collectively breathe a sigh of relief. She looked at her mom. She had the look on her face like when Sylvester the Cat ate the canary. Her card partners were "Atta girl-ing" her.

Lisa had the strangest feeling that she was not getting the joke.

She ran to the cottage to see for herself. There was Bob's Cadillac, but Joe's little Karmann Ghia was gone. She heard a sniffle sound and saw Bob sitting on their wooden bench facing the water. He had his back to her but she could hear him whispering " If only…" and "I wish…."

It was a very confusing time for her. Until, one night, she was standing at the kitchen sink drinking some water. It was almost 3 AM. She saw Bob's Cadillac lights shine through the darkened kitchen window. They turned off but it seemed as if Bob was having a hard time getting out of the car. Lisa went out by the fence to see if he needed help. The glow from the light on the house made it difficult to believe what she was seeing. She thought the man looked like Bob but he had on a curly wig. A lady's wig, and further examination revealed a very cool dress and high heels! She felt like she shouldn't be watching this. It made her feel like she had come across a secret that she could never reveal.

She quickly and quietly made her way to the house and back into her bed. She wrapped up tightly in the blankets. She would never tell anyone what she had seen. She wasn't even sure if what she had seen was real or a joke. It made her feel weird. She didn't want Bob to be any weirder. He was a funny man.

Not too long after that night, Bob had a "For Sale" sign in front of the cottage. He came to tell her mother and the neighborhood ladies that he would be moving soon to Saugatuck. He was in love for the last time!

There was a round of happy congratulations and sorry to see you go all mixed together.

After he left, the adults were talking low. Lisa heard Shirley say, "Well there goes the neighborhood!" and they all laughed for a good 15 seconds.

Lynn

The preparations were being made for Grandma's birthday. Lynn was taking charge of most of the food for her family. She was making a big pan of macaroni and cheese. She would fry up the okra on Saturday. Her Sunday offering would be her famous collard greens. She would be cooking at the farm on Saturday and Sunday since they all decided to hold it out there instead of inside Moon Park this year.

Last year, the smell of food brought everyone out of their houses and in line with a plate, to celebrate her grandmother's birthday. The problem was, there were so many people and they ran out of food. Lynn understood hunger and was willing to share the feast, even with people she had never seen before. The biggest problem was that William provided a few coolers full of liquor. When the group started to sip a bit, those sips turned to gulps, gulps turned to flapping lips, and flapping lips turned into a huge brawl. It took all four of Heaven's police cars and a fire truck to break up the fight.

Grandmother, disgusted, walked into Lynn's house and locked herself in the bathroom. It took coaxing from the minister to get her out of there. She looked at her family and said,

"This will be my last birthday."

There was a collective gasp as family members began to wonder if grandmother was ill or if she hadn't been taking her medication. The dramatic auntie started to wail. There was fright in everyone's eyes.

"Now. Let me finish." Grandmother said, "You will bring all the food and drink to the farm and we will clear a place for tents and we'll clean the outhouse and you can have my party there. For family and friends only. I don't mind getting cards in the mail," she laughed. "But spare me the police and fire department!"

So this year, they would have an extra special celebration. Since most people had nixed the idea of tents, they still were going to caravan back and forth from town. Aunt Jackie was working hard on making a couple cakes for Saturday and Sunday. She was peeling sweet potatoes for her fabulous sweet potato pies. She took her baking seriously and everyone gave her space to do whatever she needed. Lynn cleared out the things she would need and talked to Aunt Jackie as she worked. Her food could not be beat and her baking was out of this world. Trained by professional bakers, she opened a small cake business that was doing well. She had something to prove to her family every year this celebration came up.

"Lynn." She said kindly. "Please don't talk to me while I am baking. I need to concentrate."

Lynn laughed. "Whatever you need, Auntie. Whatever you need."

Greeting guests and family took most of the day on Friday.

When they were set to head to the farm they packed the arsenal of food they had prepared. Fried chicken, black eyed peas, macaroni and cheese, Catfish (that had been swimming that morning), mountains of greens, warm biscuits with red eye gravy were all placed carefully in the open trunks of four cars lined up in front of the house. Mama was already out at the farm putting together cornbread and big bowls of braised oxtails in soup.

The pig was slaughtered and had been smoking since Thursday. Its succulent aroma smacking each person in the face as they pulled up to park at the farm. What a tremendous time.

The celebration would start on Friday night, and stragglers likely wouldn't leave until Monday.

As Lynn prepared for the celebration, she felt excited. She had so many questions for her family from Chicago. Like most families, they had high and low times. This had been a very positive year. There were new babies to hold, boys that had been drafted and were awaiting orders, engagements, and new businesses.

Lynn had an uncle in the music business. He was on his way to Motown after the birthday celebration. Uncle Titus promised autographed records the last time he came. She so hoped he would deliver this weekend.

The heady feeling of laughter and good food was what made this time so special for Lynn and her grandmother. She walked up to her and said,

"No one knows how to party like you do, Grandma."

Her grandmother nodded her head and said,

"That certainly is a fact."

Lisa

It was Stag Day at the Heavenly Country Club.

Lisa knew this meant a lighter meal for the kids and her mother, since her dad would be eating out at the Club. All the neighborhood dads belonged there, even those who couldn't golf. They looked so goofy with their brightly colored sans-a-belt pants and matching polo shirts. It was a social group that played there. All the doctors and lawyers, business owners and movers and shakers of the town liked to rub elbows with friends and colleagues there. It really built community relationships and friendships.

The Country Club was located just north of town off a two lane highway. Rolling hills and tiny flags could be seen in the summer. Dad played on Wednesdays and Fridays for league play. Other days he took clients out to spend some time in his outdoor "office." When Carla, her mother, got interested in golf she was probably the only right handed person who owned left handed clubs. She practiced hard to fit in with the regulars. The ladies golf league played in the morning on Tuesday.

Golf! Golf! Golf! Leagues had begun and it was only a matter of time before her dad would have them all shining up the clubs that she, Marcy, and Billy would share. She knew from last year that she would get a putter, a driver, and a few balls and tees. Kids shouldn't be put through this kind of agony, she thought. The only cool thing about golf was the unlimited fountain Cokes and fries and the Pro Shoppe.

Lisa checked the mail every day. She sensed that the grass was beginning to brown and drought conditions of summer were setting in. The perfect time to make kids take golf lessons. So, it came as no surprise that today, looking through the mail as she returned from the mailbox, Lisa found the flyer for lessons for Heaven Country Club Kids Golf program. She swore under her breath. She knew there was no way out. She thought golf was boring.

Always held at the very hottest time of the summer, in mid-July, when the grass was a crispy golden burnished color and the ground was so hard that she could break a club (maybe not a bad thing?) it became an obstacle she had to overcome for a few more years. She imagined the feeling of pain as the club rammed into the ground and a jolt went up her spine, right to her teeth. She knew there was no way out. They were all being trained in the genteel ways of life.

There were many kids from the Lakeshore Boulevard area that took lessons out at HCC. Some of the boys were very cute in their Lacoste shorts with matching shirts. The little alligator was a symbol of money and influence. They were even starting to make a women's line. Since she would be there every day, the Pro Shoppe was, by far, the most interesting place to go.

So, on the first day, yawning from having to get up at 8:30 AM, they stood in a small group under a tree in the parking lot. Lisa was so bored she let her eyes wander around the would-be golfers, rating their golfing performances in her head. The small town had a very competitive nature. The same boys were chomping at the bit to get started and the same girls were wearing their cute golf outfits, just like they did every year. There was a helper today, as the pro who gave lessons wasn't there quite yet.

Dot Krantz practically lived at the course. Lisa asked to be excused to the ladies locker room. She had to pace herself on how many times she left the group. The others would certainly tell her dad and he would talk to her about money not growing on trees. She meandered her way to the bathroom in the locker room by way of the Pro Shoppe. That's when her love of everything "Golf" was born, for there, in front of her was a white Lacoste, fitted polo shirt for women, with a green alligator on the single pocket. She fished through the sizes. They had a "small" and it was possibly the very cutest, up to date, modern, coolest piece of clothing she ever saw. And she wanted it. She wanted it badly.

Dot was still talking when Lisa returned to the group under the tree. She was talking about the Kids Club Incentives for the summer. As she droned on, three words caught Lisa's ear.

"Pro Shop Vouchers."

This year the kids would have contests just like a golf outing. Held daily, there would be winners chosen for longest drive, closest to the pin, and best putt. The kid golfers would carry points earned each day that could be used as *money in the Pro Shoppe.*

Ugh! But it was all the kids mixed together. Not just boys

or just girls. She would never even make a point, let alone have enough for the expensive shirt. But the desire for that shirt was beginning to transcend everything. She wanted, no, craved, that special shirt. Bathroom breaks went into hyper drive so she could walk past the Pro Shoppe window and look adoringly at "her" shirt. She must figure out a way to get it.

During that first week of lessons, most of the group was divided by age: 9 to 10, 10 to 11, and 12 to 13. Although she was ten, her birthday was in December so she was able to play in either the 9 to 10 or the 10 to 11 group. She chose 9 to 10. One would think that would give her some advantage, but it didn't. Working on the putting green brought her to tears nearly every day. No matter how hard she practiced at home with her putter, plastic glass tipped sideways, and ball, the results showed little improvement. She tensed up, the ball raced past the cup, and often she was the lone leftover at the putting green after the others moved on.

The pro, Bruce Green, began each lesson with his rules talk. All Lisa heard was Blah, Blah, boring blah, as the spit collected in the corners of his mouth, all foamy and white. I guess he never wondered about the students all sitting well back from "Spit Row." She decided she might hate him, but her Catholic teaching said not to hate. So she let herself feel a strong dislike. She figured just because a person was boring can't make you hate him.

With him keeping track of the winning points daily on a clipboard, she knew she would never be able to do this the easy way. A diabolical plan was beginning to emerge. She loved that shirt more than the orange plastic wingtips she bought at the dime store and wore until they cracked somewhere between her toes and the top end of the shoes. She wanted something first rate to wear. The town had both a Sears and Montgomery Ward catalog store, but to buy anything with a brand, meant you shopped out of town and paid primo dollars.

This shirt was her chance to be as good as the rest. But that's where some planning had to come in.

It was no surprise to anyone that she was always going to be the last off of the putting green daily. That was one of the first contests. Make three putts, move to the tee box. The guy was okay, as a pro, but as a teacher, he lacked ingenuity. He had no creativity. If you went to one day, you pretty much knew how the rest would be organized. It was also suspected that he had a minor drinking problem that made him forgetful. Like when he left his clipboard on the putting green bench every day during his rules talks.

After ten excruciatingly boring minutes, he moved the group (except Lisa who was still busy with the putts) to course play. Every day it was the same routine and by day three, as she watched them go, Lisa looked around. There was her, the bench and the clipboard, and a parking lot of empty cars.

Geez. This was going to be easier than she thought! She went over to the ball washing station (quite easily her favorite thing about golf) and right next to it were the little pencils and scorecards.

Her heart rate doubled as she grabbed a pencil. Her hands started to sweat. She tested the pencil by writing on a scorecard. Yes, it made a mark. She quickly descended on the clipboard. Mr. Green had terrible penmanship. Sister Rosina would probably have him writing his name over and over until it improved, she chuckled to herself. She noticed that sometimes he had the kids fill in scores as well. Oh man! It could not get any better than this!

She found her name. To the left of a series of zeroes, she put a 1. She skipped a few spots so it wouldn't be obvious. Plus, she knew that Mrs. Green ran the Pro Shoppe. She was so lazy. Like the day she said, "Miss. That is my Coke on the bar, will you bring it to me?" And Lisa, who was standing right in front of her in the Pro Shoppe walked all the way to the bar to retrieve her drink. There was not a chance in hell that she would bother to ask if these scores were correct. And anyway, the top four people in each age group with the highest scores would get Pro Shoppe Vouchers.

She saw Johnny Kosski running up the hill on 18. It was time to get as much space between her and the clipboard. She didn't say anything as he swooped in, grabbed the clipboard, and ran off. Sweat was pouring down her face. She thought she might barf right there. But, nothing happened. No one came to put her in handcuffs! She was leading her group by 10 points. If she could do this for the following week, she'd be on her way to that shirt!

So here she was on Monday of Week 2, sheepishly putting. It was time for a potty break before ambling back out to the course. She checked the clock. The second week of lessons was just as thrilling as the first. She knew if she stalled long enough, the kid golfers would be coming off the course and she wouldn't be subject to the teeth jarring on her tee shot. She also knew that tomorrow would show she had an easy lead in all categories.

She lollygagged in the lady's locker room, using the lotions and perfumes and lighting matches from the bowls filled with HCC matchbooks. Next, she went to the Pro Shoppe window. She didn't walk into the small room because she didn't want Mrs. Green to see her inside again. She might put two and two together and then where would she be? She looked at the ladies polos and sure enough, her shirt was still there. "I'll wear it with my green shorts to match the alligator," she thought to herself as she hurried back.

Mr. Green was talking again. Two more days of lessons and then, if you had won Pro Shoppe points, you would receive your certificate in the mail.

Oh my gosh! Lisa thought. It couldn't be a more perfect plan. She had plenty of points!

That night, she set the table and made the salad. Dad was out grilling steaks and life was happily moving on. Two days became one. She padded her score again, ever so slightly.

Finally, the day came! Jailbreak! No more golf lessons!

Now the WAIT began. It was just a matter of time.

Two days passed by. Not a thing for anyone.

Then five days went by. What the heck, did they forget?

On the 6th day, two envelopes came from Heaven Country Club. One for her brother and one for Lisa! They opened them hastily and sure enough there were vouchers for one item under $25.00 at the Pro Shoppe! Her brother eyed her suspiciously. He knew that her receiving a voucher was fishy.

"Huh!" She exclaimed to him. "They must have given them to everybody."

"I guess so, because you would never have had enough points, unless they were loser points."

As soon as her dad came home, Lisa asked if he could take her out to the Pro Shoppe to spend her voucher.

"Maybe tomorrow." He said "I am beat. Make me a highball."

After she had mixed his Jim Beam with water and put a few ice cubes in, she brought the drink to him and asked,

"When tomorrow, do you think, dad?"

"Didn't I just say I am tired?" He asked short temperedly. "Put on Barbra Streisand."

She went over to the long, wooden stereo cabinet, knowing she had to lay low now. It was not a good omen to have Barbra Streisand on. If she poked this bear again, she could likely lose the voucher altogether. She got the album out of the sleeve, suspended it on the post, and turned the dial to play. It slid off the post with a mechanical clink and soon Barbra was crooning sweetly in the background. She backed out of the room on quiet feet.

Oh man! She thought to herself. I need to get that shirt. The wheels kept turning. The angel on her right shoulder said to ' be patient.' But the devil on the left one said, 'don't waste any time.'

It was only 4:00 PM. The Country Club didn't seem too far away. She would jump on her bike and get home before dinner at 6:00 PM! No one would be the wiser. But she had to hustle it.

She got on her bike. She wanted the blue Schwinn Stingray with the banana seat like her friend Sadie had. Instead, she received a white Huffy with a fat long seat. No one had ever heard of this brand. Oh well, it worked and she wasn't arguing the fact that she had a new bike.

As she left her dead end street, she knew she should turn left at the stop sign. She was heading for downtown. Suddenly afraid, she thought about what streets to take. Past Aunt Sis's house, turn left on the highway and go straight. Satisfied with her directional route, she checked and double checked her voucher envelope and put it in her back pocket and pedaled as fast as she could.

What the heck was up with all these hills? She thought as she felt the sweat running down her back. She had never paid attention. Her legs began to burn from the exertion. Going by her aunt's house seemed all uphill. There was a stop light on Blue Star Highway. She waited until traffic cleared on the green light and rode well to the right, on the shoulder. It was wide enough and she began to settle in for the long ride.

Something strange happened then. A blue police car pulled up behind her on the shoulder.

"Miss. Please stop your bike." He said.

Lisa was petrified. Would he put her in jail? Will her dad find out? And finally, would the Pro Shoppe be open when she got there? She looked around. The officer had a big smile on his face.

"Do your parents know you are riding your bike on this busy highway?" He asked.

Lisa just looked at him. No words wanted to come out. She waited.

"Aren't you Artie's daughter?" he prodded.

Oh Sweet Jesus, he knew who she was! Still she stood mute. The clock was ticking.

"Let's put that bike in the trunk and I'll take you home." He said, his face still in a perma smile.

"I am going to the Country Club." She said in barely a whisper.

"Playing some golf, huh?" he said with a laugh.

"I have to get there by 5:30 PM," she faltered. She realized she had started to cry.

The policeman was stricken. What was really the problem here? He thought to himself. Maybe she was running away from home.

"I am afraid I am going to have to take you home. If I know Artie, you are not going to want to break his rules by bike riding on a US highway." His face was getting redder and redder. He began to open his trunk. Lisa began to plead and scream.

"Noooo! You don't understand! I have to get to the Pro Shoppe. I need to pick something up."

The cop began to patronize her.

"Whatever you need will be there tomorrow." He said with a little more force. This little girl was proving to be a handful. He opened the door.

Her brain was exploding with stimulated overload. What was she going to say to her parents? She only had the short ride with the cop to work it out. More importantly, she had to come up with an idea to make this part of the problem go away and get that shirt. Could she say she left something important at the Club? Could she call her friend Sadie and ask if her dad was playing cards there, and maybe he could grab the shirt for her? Could she call the Pro Shop and just ask them to put the shirt on hold?

None of those things were even probable. As they turned down Apache Court, she felt the wall of doom. Little did she know that this feeling was the beginning of a series of similar feelings she would have when she turned toward home.

The policeman stopped in front of her house. They passed all the neighborhood houses as if in the 4th of July parade. She could see them pressing their faces to the windows or even coming out their front stoops, all holding a tense breath and wondering what had happened.

Mr. Pullman, the policeman, pulled her bike out of the car. Her mother rushed out, rubbing her hands on her apron. She saw Lisa in the front and swiftly moved over to the side of the car.

"What happened? Are you OK?"

Her father appeared shortly after. He took in the scene in a heartbeat. He appraised the bike. It looked the same. He appraised his daughter. She was not bleeding or broken either.

With relief on his face, he said,

"Evenin' Dan. What seems to have happened here?"

"Hail Mary, Full of grace" Lisa had begun to pray with a vengeance.

"Your daughter here was riding her bicycle on Blue Star Highway, Artie. She was well past North Shore Drive when I spotted her."

Her father's face became a hardened mask. It reminded her of the scary tribal masks at the Museum of Science and Industry in Chicago. He looked over at Lisa's mother, whose eyes were like saucers.

"Did you tell her she could ride out there?" Artie shouted at her mother, barely able to contain his anger.

"Of course not!" her mother cried.

"She was very upset when she found out she wasn't going to make it to the Pro Shoppe at the Golf Club." Officer Pullman continued. He winked and chuckled a little when he said this. "I am sure you will take it from here." He doffed his cap and made to exit quickly. He knew that look in Artie's eyes. He might ground his daughter but he looked more relieved than angry.

"Get in the house." Artie's voice was so low. She had never heard him like this before. It was ominous. What would happen to her now?

When Lisa walked in, her brothers and sisters just looked at her with mouths open.

"You are in so much trouble." Her little brothers said with glee. "Dad's going to ground you forever!"

Lisa was resolved to take what was coming to her. She went directly to her room.

Time went by slowly.

Her parents did not come into her room. Shadows grew longer outside. Sunlight was dimming when her father opened the door.

"I should be taking you over my knee and giving you the spanking of your life!" He said, "When I think of how dangerous this was and how we could have had a policeman coming to tell us he found you dead on the side of the road, let alone coming here to embarrass us in our own neighborhood? And you being driven home in the police car?"

Silent tears rolled down her face. She had really meant to go and come back without anyone knowing. The whole thing had become a snarled mess. Yet, if she told him why she was going, he would find out that she had cheated on those scores in the first place. No words were left to explain it.

"You will be grounded until further notice." He said, "and now we are going to go out to the Country Club to see why, in the holy hell, you pulled such a stupid stunt as to ride your bike on the highway! Do you know what people are going to say about me? That I let my kids ride their bikes on a dangerous highway without even knowing where they were? This is going to be bad for all you kids!" He knew the others were listening outside the door. "BECAUSE YOU ARE ALL GROUNDED!"

"Let's go."

That's it? Lisa thought. This is the worst I am going to get from him? She began to feel hopeful. They rode in silence. Well almost, as her dad was muttering under his breath the entire 10 minute ride.

When they arrived, there were many men there still playing cards after their golf games.

"Hey Art!" they cried "I heard you took a hammering on the back nine this afternoon" But her dad's eyes were steeled on the pro shop.

"Hey Tom, I forgot to pick up something from the pro shop. Do you mind unlocking the door?"

"No problem, Artie." Tom said without even indicating that this was an unusual request. The door opened and Tom said to give him a holler when we found what we needed.

Artie turned to his daughter:

"Well, where is the thing that made you break rules, got you grounded, and will have repercussions on your brothers and sisters? I got to see this."

This was all too weird. Was he going to rip it up when he found it? Lisa couldn't bear it if he gave it to someone else in the family. He'd brought home things from the Pro Shoppe before that he would only give to certain kids. She had never gotten one of those things. Her eyes scanned the wall. Yes, there it was. Her beautiful Lacoste dream shirt! Like a magnet, she was drawn to it.

She heard her dad make a noise like: "Huh. Huh. Huh." It was kind of a laugh but sounded evil somehow. Lisa could not allow him to ruin her chance for the shirt. She wondered if he knew she wanted it so badly, that he might not let her have it. Was he going to use it to teach her a lesson?

She changed her tactic. She would have to outfox the fox. Fingering a small disposable plastic golf hood, (the flimsy film kind to wear once in case it rained). She checked the price. It was only $1.98. She picked it up.

"That?" her father melted into hilarious laughter. "That is what you wanted so bad?"

"I want it for Grandma." She said contritely. Oh, this story would be good. "Her birthday is coming up."

She really didn't know when her grandma's birthday was, but she was watching her father's face soften.

"Well, give your certificate to Mr. Tom and we can get out of here."

Wait! Her certificate was for up to $25. She realized then

that it was never going to happen. Her prized Lacoste polo shirt was slipping through her fingers. She handed over the certificate.

"$1.98?" Mr. Tom laughed. 'You sure you don't want to add anything to this?"

She looked around. Her dad had gone back to cutting up with his buddies at the card table inside the club.

"Do I have enough left for that shirt?" She asked.

"I think we can make that happen." He said with a wink.

Explosions of joy went off in her head! She watched him take it down from the hanger as if it was made of glass. Finally, something was going to go right.

"There you go."

She reached out her hand.

"Wait a minute," He said. "There's a note on here that says that this is sold to someone already. How about …let's see…we have a large, large, and extra-large. I am afraid you will swim in these."

Her ears heard it but she couldn't believe it. Stunned, she just shook her head. She knew they would never work.

"Well, young lady, between you and me, I am going to let you take that rain hood home. You keep your certificate and when you get your old man out here again, I will make sure there is a shirt there in your size."

"Thank you," she whispered. She had been beaten by her own game. It had to be that karma thing.

"SO, are we ready now?" Her dad came in with a much easier attitude.

"Yes" she whispered and they quietly got into the car.

Days went past and with them, her longing for the shirt. Her parents were right. It was dangerous to ride out on the highway and something else they'd never know, how she had cheated to win. They lifted the grounding to being home when the street lights came on, and now that August had arrived, time to play after dinner was getting noticeably shorter. She was running down the street when she was stopped dead in her tracks.

There, running toward her was her best friend, Sadie, and she was wearing the shirt.

Lynn

No one in Heaven really had a beef with the cops. Most of the squad was made up of local boys who did some training and apprenticeships. With Affirmative Action came opportunities for boys from the Zone to join the city and state police forces. Heaven was very open to the influx of veterans fresh out of Vietnam who had skills.

That was until a skirmish between a white supremacist group and the local citizens erupted into an all-out riot. This KKK offshoot liked to patrol around the small Michigan towns where there were populations with ten percent and more black citizens. They roiled up hatred as they marched through the towns, claiming First Amendment Freedom of Speech rights.

As they marched their way to the Zone, about 30 members strong, Heaven's police force was ready. Sal Grant and Manny Trange just joined the force after coming home from their tour of duty in Vietnam. There had been some question about them being partners. Afterall, no one knew if their experiences in war might cause them to make errors in judgment. Could they rationally take care of an out of control crowd, or might it serve to trigger something unresolved? They waited in a line with the other city cops and a few state police troopers. Being the only black officers, Sal and Manny had both grown up in the area. There was violence, at times, but not very often.

Lynn watched from her bedroom window. It had the best vantage point of the house. Mama stayed home from work for fear Lamar would get himself involved in some trouble. The kids were sent to play in the windowless playroom.

Tensions were ramping up. Megaphones were screaming white power slogans. Bricks were flying. Forays were made from the curb into the crowd. Many residents lined the shoulders of the street, rejecting the Aryan messages by trying to chant their own louder ones. Something bad was getting ready to bust open.

The strains of Motown music began faintly playing from deep within the Zone itself. Soulful and booming with bass, the music seemed to be coming from open windows. As the volume grew, it began drowning out the marchers' voices. Transistor radios, dialed to the same soulful stations were adding to the intersection of sound. Lynn wanted in on it. She ran over to the old stereo speakers that were hooked up to her small hi-fi. Turning the volume on high, she threw on "Love Child" by the Supremes.

Lamar came running up the stairs.

"Lynn! That record's too soft. No one can even hear it. We can do better." He began shuffling through her 45s.

"Lamar, you're scratching my records. Stop!"

He grabbed "Dancing in the Street" by Martha and the Vandellas.

"Well, this will do for a start," he said, putting it on the turntable and running out of the room. He returned with a stack of records.

"Ooh, Lamar. These are good. Play James Brown next."

"Let's get them in order." Lamar said.

They got the songs in order: Sam Cooke's "A Change is Going to Come", Aretha Franklin's "Respect", The Supremes "Come See About Me." They thought they would play them over and over but when they went to survey the crowd, all they saw were people dancing.

The group of marchers passed through without further incident. As more and more people turned to blast their stereos, the less and less the White Supremacists mattered. The Zone had reclaimed its own. It didn't do it with violence. It's essence communed in one large force and no message could have overtaken it that day.

"I am going down there!" Lynn said, "It looks like the marchers are gone!"

She bumped down the stairs with Lamar close behind. Mama stopped them.

"Mama, it's all good now." Lynn said.

Mama looked at them and then took them to the door. There was Sal and Manny and they were being handcuffed. Beside them were two of the marchers, their bodies still and bloody.

"Mama? What happened?" Lynn asked.

"It appears that Manny and Sal are headed to jail." Mama spoke over the approaching ambulance's siren. "Those men are beaten to a pulp. I went out there myself since all you fools were dancing and being silly. I begged for them to stop but they appeared to be possessed by the devil himself."

"So," Lamar said, "The only black cops in the whole place get themselves arrested? Don't you think there is more to the story?"

Mama gave Lamar the look she used when ignorant people spoke. She pursed her lips and let her eyebrows arch.

"But everyone's out there dancing." Lynn said "Mama, our people have thwarted the Klan!"

"Lynn, do you think that this display of drowning out the voices of one group with louder voices of another is the answer? Do you really think that our troubles are over?

Mama was on a roll now. "Only love, Lynn. Only love can drive out that hatred. Dr. King tells us that. When will people learn that simple lesson?"

Zenobia paused to take a breath and Lynn seized the moment.

"Well, Mama, I think if singing and dancing isn't about love, then nothing is.."

She hugged her mother and she and Lamar went out to join the groups of street dancers..

Lisa

The beach at the end of the street was where the neighborhood kids played. The neighborhood mothers had a false sense of security rationalizing that if the kids were together, no one would probably get hurt or drown. Every few hours someone's mom would peek over the high lake bank and make sure all heads were counted. The kids played on the beach, rain or shine. In bathing suits or shorts, not a day was missed. The banks were striped with clay squished into place by the moving glaciers formed by the Ice Age. Shoeless, the kids would make up games to play with the wet, gloppy stuff. There was no such thing as a rip tide, a red flag, or parent supervision. This beach was just a continuation of their street. Nothing bad had ever happened here. Yet.

It was probably the most dangerous time of Lisa's life and she never knew it.

One day, one of the boys up the street brought a piece of plywood to the beach. It slid down the bank like a luge. It took six people to hold onto it and float it out to where the boat pilings were. These were posts that came out of the water. In the old days, boats tied up to these when their owners wanted to go ashore. They had been there since Lisa could remember. But folks didn't tie up any longer. Lake Michigan had proven to be a beast which changed not with tides, but with wind. Often seen as a huge bathtub, the water sloshed over the edge into the bank violently. Many boats had been torn up in an afternoon.

The water had a pull that rearranged the sand underneath. Sometimes digging out an area of sand and redistributing it to another place. These areas were called drop offs and sand-bars. Drop offs changed on a weekly basis as winds coming out of certain directions would force the waves to drag the sand along below.

Lisa often swam out to the pilings on calm days. They were her landmarks and the outer limits of her swimming expertise. As she grew older, she was able to hold her own with the boys in the neighborhood, often swimming out to that area with ease. That was in calm water. When the waves picked up with wind or weather, Lisa stayed close to shore. She didn't attempt to cross any drop off areas but often just body surfed the little whitecaps from the sandbar to shore. She knew that this week there were at least two drop offs before getting out to the deep water where the pilings were.

Knowledge of drop offs and sandbars are a way of surviving when you are swimming in the "big lake." If a person could float over the drop off, which would put the sandy bottom at least six to ten feet below, and make it to the sandbar, which might be ankle deep, a swimmer basically had learned the toughest part of swimming in Lake Michigan, according to Apache Court rules. It was when a person stopped and pushed down to touch the bottom that often caused some trouble. Expecting to touch bottom when there was no sand was an alarming experience. Arms up, watching the sun fade, and losing downward momentum was one of Lisa's deepest fears.

Sandbars were not to be counted on because the sand shifted every day. Some days there was a really wide drop off, and while swimming over it one day might have been effortless, the next might find you thinking the sandbar was still in the same place, only to find your head well below the water doing a hands up test. The kids tended to stay together, but this day had them forget the buddy system of swimming.

The day of the plywood caper was hot. The humidity in the air made for soggy wet lungs. When you breathed in at the end of a day like that, it hurt deep inside and made you cough. Lisa was not able to join the others in bringing out the wood. It was an all-boys activity and no girls were even allowed to touch the wood.

There were few girls that wanted to. Sadie stayed on the beach. She was happy to look for rocks and read magazines. She had a float and Lisa asked her if she might use it to float out to the pilings where the platform was being built.

"I don't think so." Sadie said, "I might want to use it in a little while."

So, with nothing to hold onto, Lisa attempted to make it out there on her own. If their mothers only knew how harrowing of a feat this was, then they would never have allowed the kids to get in the water. But they were all clueless to its dangers and thankful they didn't have to try and entertain their kids. With a smooth lake, one could flip over and float on their back, kicking their feet would be just like an outboard motor to get them over drop offs. Taking their time, they would go from floating over a drop off to slogging over a sandbar to floating over another drop off.

That day, however, there was a slight chop. Floating became nearly impossible as the water kept flying into Lisa's face. It was in her eyes and up her nose, and she drank more lake water than she cared to. She began to wonder if she was close to a sandbar. Looking up, she realized the boys were too far ahead to give her some help. She reached her toe down into the water. Now, this presented a huge problem with forward momentum. With no one watching, Lisa's body dropped below the surface. She could open her eyes and see beneath the murky surface. There, in front of her, about 10 yards away, was the sandbar. She kicked with her feet to get up above the surface and take a breath of air. Determined to make it, she went back underwater to swim. It was faster to swim underwater.

In no time at all, she came up on the sand bar and soon was just standing in waist high water. Buffeted by the tiny waves but victorious that she had made it! No one had seen or ever knew how close she was to panicking and sinking.

About seven neighborhood kids fit atop the sagging wood. They used it as a diving platform and jumped into the deeper water, and swam around to a person who dragged them back up. There was no easy way to get atop the board. The pilings were covered with slippery seaweed and algae. Lisa chose to be one of the helpers and didn't dive into the water at all. Spending all day on that plywood deck in the sun, they sang popular top 40 songs they knew from WLS, a hot Chicago radio station. They were carefree living this life. They scoffed at the kids who owned pools. That kind of swimming wasn't real.

Suddenly, Doug Becker looked up and saw some strangers making their way down the lake bank using Apache Court's steps! What the hell? It appeared as if they were invading the beach! There were three of them. All boys in their early teens they'd never seen. Someone guessed they were from a street over (where the poor kids lived).

"Who do those guys think they are, using our stairs?" said one of the Apache Court boys. "You better get the hell out of here," screamed another. "They must be from Baver Court," growled Tom MaHoover.

As if on cue, the boys dove into the water and there was a melee of splashes, like fish caught in a barrel. The boys were swimming with swift ease to get to the beach and to kick the intruders off their land. The plywood platform sprang up fast, with the loss of their balanced weight, it slid off the pilings, Lisa with it, into the water!

No one turned around to see that Lisa was caught in between the piling and plywood. Just able to keep her footing, her eyes were level with the water. She breathed by leaning back to put her mouth up to snatch air between waves. She frantically kicked at the plywood to set it free.

She felt a panic then. The waves seemed to be coming in faster and cresting earlier. They beat her in the face. With one last ditch effort, she steadied herself, drew in both feet and pushed as hard as she could. The platform dislodged, the wood drifting out to sea quickly on the waves. She searched the shore, hoping she'd been seen and someone was coming out to help her. She was waving and yelling to get someone's attention, but her words were slapped away by water that had turned, in a few hours, from tiny cresting white caps to long, rolling, vicious waves.

One of the Baver Court boys looked up from the fracas, and shouted, "Hey! That girl's going to drown!"

He ran to the water, leaving the fight behind. Slogging in knee deep, he looked back to find the Apache Court boys who were watching him in disbelief.

"She needs our help!" He cried emphatically.

Then all the boys turned and dove into the surf.

Billy, Lisa's big brother, gave the kid a punch in the water and said: "She's my sister! I'll save her."

Lisa was bobbing up high enough with each wave to keep her eye on the horizon. She knew to swim across a riptide but forgot to flip and float and let the waves bring her in. The water was just too deep for her to flip over onto her back. The waves were strong and disrupted her. She felt like she should just give up. She couldn't do it.

When the group of the neighborhood boys reached her, they threw her up in front of them to keep her face out of the water. She could see Sadie on the shore, ready to give her a towel, the float just sitting there on the shore. The Baver Court boys had long since retreated. She could see the one who had alerted the others, watching from high atop the bank. She owed him some gratitude.

Once on shore, she took the towel from Sadie, thankfully, and wrapped herself up and laid in the sand. She coughed and choked on water and snot. Everyone had been where she was today. They all made it out fine. She should just get over it. The boys were muttering and cussing about the invasion. They hadn't realized that the plywood was not on the pilings still. When Billy looked over, he could see that it was just a glint on the horizon.

"Great!" Her brother said. "Now we don't even have a platform for tomorrow!"

The boys all looked at Lisa with malice. They had lost face with that other bunch. They would say that the Apache boys were chicken, all because Lisa had ruined everything.

Like a swarm of bees, bitching and moaning, they took the steps up the bank that led back home. No one checked to see if Lisa was okay or needed a hand. Sadie stayed just long enough to ask if she wanted her to stay before joining the group on the steps. Lisa was alone.

She looked around. Nothing but a deserted beach. She hoped someone would come back to help her get up the steps. No one came back down.

Gradually sitting, taking deep breaths, she was startled by a voice that was coming from behind the scrubby bushes on the bank.

"Man! Are you sure you are okay?"

It was the boy who stopped fighting to rescue her! She could see the bruise forming on his cheek where Billy had punched him. She didn't know what to say.

"Thanks. Sorry they are such assholes." She managed.

He sat down next to her and she was alarmed. He was about

a year or two older than her, she guessed. His hair was black and curly and he was very tan. Upon further scrutiny, she noted that his body seemed muscular. Not muscled like a bodybuilder but more like a swimmer. A triangle formed from his shoulders down to his small waist. It reminded her of Joe. Why were the 'off-limits' boys so cute?

He turned to face her.

"My name is Jed Adams," he said, "and I don't live on Baver. I was just visiting my cousins." She turned toward him, and the blueness of his eyes seemed incongruent with the rest of his coloring; it took her breath away. She found herself thinking how handsome he was. Like all the features made for a face like Greg Brady only way cooler and more appealing.

"Lisa Palma," she said.

"I know who you are," He said.

All at once she felt the need to get out of there.

"Well, thanks for saving my life," she said, as she grabbed the towel and her flip flops.

"Yeah, see you around," he said.

Lisa ran through the hot sand, not even feeling it burn her feet. She had a weird, bubbly feeling now. She hoped her brother hadn't seen her talking to Jed. She felt his eyes still on her when she got to the last step. She turned. But there was no one there at all.

Lisa

Sometimes she wondered if the small town she lived in made her more confident. Making friends was easy as long as she was the center of attention. It was the only place to have autonomy. In Catholic school, with only 13 kids in her class, it was easy to muscle the others out of the way. She was editor of the yearbook, voted most likely to succeed, and most popular; literally everything achieved with her parent's (especially her dad's) validation in mind. Her brothers were a constant source of ridicule. Achievements she made in her short life were given some notice, but as soon as her brothers became aware of them, they whittled them down into broken pieces, waiting to bypass her on the pedestal with their own accolades. It often made her feel second class.

Deidre was the only black girl in the eighth grade class, and likely in the entire school. With braids, glasses, and a ready smile, she was just like anyone else. Her house was in the country where she lived with her grandparents. She brought sandwiches on homemade bread, pickles wrapped in waxed paper, and a piece of fruit every day for lunch. She was not allowed the hot dog that the school served once a month as the one special hot lunch. Lisa rarely took time away from herself to ponder

Deidre's predicament of having no parents. Junior High was rough enough just taking care of yourself rather than worrying too much about others.

The girls in her school went through a weird stretch, when one girl would convince the rest to avoid someone and not speak to her. Often, this singled out girl would walk into the classroom just like every other day, only to have everyone look away and whisper to each other. Deidre was never the singled out girl. She was always willing, though, to be that girl's friend for however long it took to get back with the popular group.

As eighth grade moved into the final semester, a counselor from the high school visited the school. It was time to start choosing classes. There were no AP tracts, but just going to a private school gave a leg up to be placed in the classes that were not traditionally offered to freshmen. Lisa wanted to be a biochemist. She loved science but had little use for physical science. She went to her science instructor at St. Leonard's to write her a pass, and begged to be placed in Biology and not Physical Science. That's when she hit a snag. Deidre wanted the same treatment. Her interest was nursing.

The ninth grade Physical Science teacher was rumored to be super strict. Mrs. Smit told the girls that she would only allow one of the incoming freshmen from their school to receive advanced placement status and to skip P.S. Neither girl backed down. They wanted their track to go straight into life sciences. The girls were going to have to take a comprehensive test to decide who would get the nod.

Deidre looked at Lisa with a smirk. This feeling wasn't

unfamiliar for her. She knew before the test was administered that Lisa was far more driven to ace the test. She didn't want to compete against that energy. Being the only girl of color in the class, she realized she would not be the girl chosen to crown Mary in the May Crowning, or take up the "Gifts" in the eighth grade Graduation Mass. Deidre wanted this privilege and felt she deserved it.

The afternoon the test was to be administered, Lisa waited for Deidre.

"Look," Lisa said, "We need to stand up for ourselves. It's bullshit to think they can't let two of us in. The whole idea of taking a stupid test doesn't make sense at all. I am going to the high school tomorrow and talk to Mrs. Smit. I know she is sup- posed to be mean, but I think we need to state our cases."

Deidre smiled wanly.

"I have to take the bus home. There's no other way for me to get home. It's okay. You can take the pass. I will take Physical Science."

"It just doesn't feel right," Lisa said.

"It is just a fact you won't have to face," Deidre said. "When you are stuck taking care of your grandparents and you're in eighth grade, well, the whole idea of being a nurse is more like a pipe dream."

"You're sure?" Lisa asked.

"You'll do great," Deidre said.

The following day after school, Lisa set out to walk the two miles to get to the high school. She called the previous day and asked Mrs. Smit if she could meet with her. She wasn't sure how she was going to do it, but she was determined to get Deidre in also.

She arrived just as Mrs. Smit was preparing her stacks of papers in her briefcase.

"Hello, Mrs. Smit? I am Lisa Palma." She said quietly.

"Yeah? So I have heard. You are Billy's sister, right? He turned my fourth hour class into a clown show. He's very smart, but a real pain in the …"

"Mrs. Smit, I am not here about Billy. I have come to ask you if you would do something. My friend, Deidre Mills, is in my St. Leonard's eighth grade class too and we both want to have a shot at the A.P. pass to Biology in ninth grade. We have some dreams. We have made our life plans. Is there any way possible you would let us both get the bye from your class?"

"Ha. Ha." Mrs. Smit chuckled. "Do you know how many students send their parents to bully me into the very same thing? "Don't ruin their G.P.A," they say. Like I am the one getting the grade. Heck, I just give them what they earn. Why should I entertain the thought of either of you getting a pass out of Physical Science?"

Lisa began to cry softly. She hadn't meant for it to happen.

"Well, for one thing. because I want it more than anything. I can outdo Deidre in a test for the spot but I don't think it's fair for her. She wants to be a nurse. She should have all the chances to be a nurse. I think we both have potential. She can't help it if she doesn't get to volunteer places because she has to take care of her grandparents. If anything, that is the best experience she can have for nursing."

Mrs. Smit looked at her for a long time.

"Seems like you are really advocating for your friend. Why not just give up your spot? That's one way you will know for sure."

"But I really want it too." She said now getting a little miffed, "Who made the rule that only one person can get the pass? What's the rationale?"

"Look," Mrs. Smit said, heading toward the door, keys in hand. "I have to go. Rules don't just change overnight. I will consider your request."

"I appreciate that," Lisa said.

She headed out the backdoor to the school and cut across the parking lot. As she walked, she thought of all the things she should have said and how much more powerful they would have been. She scooted over to the side of the road as a white convertible zoomed by. It was Mrs. Smit, who offered neither a wave nor a ride. That kind of lady isn't giving anyone a break. She thought she better get ready to make a decision. Fight for herself or fight for Deidre?

She decided to let it ride.

The days were interminable. The schedules came from the high school and next week they would be going over to orientation. Each student received an envelope. She waited and watched as each of her fellow students compared with friends and classes. Deidre was speechless as she looked at Lisa. With tears in her eyes, she silently mouthed the words 'thank you.'

Well, that's it, Lisa thought, trying to be brave. She opened her envelope. Opening her schedule, an index card fell out. It read: "You've got guts and that's worth something." –RS

She looked at the schedule for when she would be meeting for Science every day but couldn't find the name 'Smit' among the teachers. She looked at the subjects by hour: 1st, Physical Ed–Aitch; 2nd, Biology-Klaw; 3rd, English-Garma; 4th, Algebra-Shannon; 5th, History-Carlson 6th; Sociology-Yelding.

She felt like all the bones had turned to Jello. But wait, did that mean?

"Deidre?" She asked. "Do you have Biology 2nd hour?"

"Yes, I do." She said.

So that was it. She had advocated for her friend and herself and it had worked!

She could not have been happier.

Lynn

High school orientation filled Lynn with excitement. She knew she wanted to get fully immersed in activities while shooting for an education. She met up with her friends at Moon Park. Even though it was over 80 degrees, some of them were wearing their back-to-school clothes. Big Wheel, the only store that actually had new clothes that were affordable, featured school clothes in their sale, and Lynn recognized the colors and patterns in the polyester blends she saw on Trudy and Elaine. Lynn chose to wear clothes she already owned. She would unveil her new school clothes slowly. She thought it was a little tacky to wear them just for a few hours of orientation.

Sports teams were practicing all around the school. The track and tennis courts were filled with hopeful students trying to make the team. The football practice field had large pieces of padded equipment that the boys were pushing in rows of four up and down the field with their shoulders. The girls stopped for a minute and admired the fine-looking bunch of athletes. The Heavenly Saints were supposed to have a good year this year! Well, they sure were winners in the looks department! Lynn kept scanning the group until she saw who she was looking for.

When she found Jimmy Flowers she saw him looking right back at her. She smiled a white, toothy grin. She liked that guy!

Passing the cheerleaders, the girls pointed out the new faces from the parochial schools nearby. In the freshmen group there were two girls they didn't know. Lynn felt bold. Walking up to them on their break, she asked, "What's your name? You are not familiar to me"

Lisa and Caryn looked at her. They didn't even know each other! Caryn went to the Lutheran School.

"My name is Lisa Palma." she said.

"Caryn," said her cheerleading partner.

"Are you girls the new freshmen on the cheerleading squad?" Lynn asked.

"We are all new on the freshmen squad." Said Lisa, laughing, "We're fresh *women.*"

Lynn didn't know how to take this exchange. Was this girl being a smartass or was this the way she talked to everyone?

"Oh. Mmm. Hmm." She said, "Well, I hope you can represent our class."

"Wait." Caryn stepped in. "We hope we didn't hurt your feelings."

"Yeah. We were just messing with you." Lisa said, "We have been since 6:00 AM and that lady won't let up."

She pointed to their coach whose lips formed one straight line. "Perky, isn't she?"

Lynn laughed. She had heard of this lady. She was the mother of one of the varsity cheerleaders, and a first class bitch.

"What's yours? Name I mean," Lisa asked.

"Lynn,"she said "Lynn Parris. Hey, is your brother Billy?"

"Hi,Lynn …and yes,"she said reluctantly."Billy's my brother."

Lynn told her that he was cute, but she really had her eye on someone else.

"What's your schedule?" Lynn asked. Before she could get an answer, Mrs. Treet blew her whistle that the break was over.

Lisa rolled her eyes. Back to practice she went.

Lynn watched her go. She was encouraged.

She turned around.

"What's your sked-uuu-awl?"Jill Turner, a sophomore, was heckling Lynn from the bench in front of the school's office door. "Gurl. They don't care about you. Those white girls only talked to you because they were afraid of you. They don't want nothing to do with you?"

Lynn's face got hot and she felt tears forming. But she was not to be bested by Jill.

"Maybe they don't care about you because you're so ugly." She retorted, laughing.

Jill's face got serious. "Really. Listen to me. Those girls aren't like us. They might say 'hi' to you now and then, but that is all you should count on. You don't want to be their friends."

Lynn chuckled. "Poor Jill. I am everyone's friend. I am your friend as much as theirs."

Jill looked at Lynn and sneered. "You are going to learn a lot this year, Lynn. And it is not always pretty."

Lisa

Freshman cheerleading tryouts were over. There were practices every day that began on August 1. The anticipation of a public high school; and mixing with kids she never knew, was appealing. Lisa prayed away the chance that she would begin using drugs or that she might falter at a larger school. But, with her older brother already at the high school and flourishing, she became more confident. It was reassuring to know that most people liked him. He was an athlete and a scholar. Maybe it wouldn't be so hard to fit in. The main source of anxiety was having to walk from the high school through the Zone after cheerleading practices.

Although just a mile or less from her house, Lisa did not become familiar with the ZONE while growing up. It was as if an invisible fence had been placed on the Lakeshore Boulevard that fed into her neighborhood. Walks home from school had always been a straight shot. The sidewalk went all the way from St. Leonard's School down the lakeshore, right to her street. She never veered.

Although she had gone to many events at the high school, it had always been on a side street and not through the area itself.

Its fixed rent housing skirted the National Engines Foundry, the Avert Piano Company, the aluminum factory, and the beginnings of a larger industrial park. Each home looked exactly the same. Lisa felt the government planners could have changed up the house styles a little. The only difference in them was their color and if their yards were maintained. The lots were tiny. Even the air seemed to hang around it like a wet oily cloth. The factories emitted a can of instant smog; belching smoke that became downright oppressive when mixed with the heat radiating from the brick and concrete buildings there.

The orange dust from the foundry settled silently on car windshields and chairs overnight. It was a nuisance to wipe things clean every morning. The pall, like a filmy curtain, hung in the air from smokestack emissions. While it thinned a bit over her house along the lakeshore, the Zone got hit with the most pollution. The houses often were sprayed clean with a garden hose.

Lisa didn't really know anyone who lived in these houses. Once, she had been in an accident with her babysitter right on the corner of one of the streets, which happened to be on their route to the high school. The people inside the house called an ambulance. While they waited for its arrival, Lisa noticed there were only adults in the house. The women were still in their pajamas although it was after 4:00 PM. It made Lisa think how within a square mile, people's lives were so very different than her own. And how strangely out of place these people seemed on a bright fall day.

On the surface, all students in the area attended the same beautiful, ten year old high school. Lisa's aunt taught at the public elementary school. But having all the events at the high school, left many bewildered bus drivers from opposing teams, at a loss if they overshot the high school drive. For once inside its radius, the Zone's inhabitants were predominantly black. Asking for directions was terrifying for the bus drivers and hilarious for those that lived there.

It made no sense to have houses and factories and a magnificent high school (with an Olympic sized pool) all in the same place. How did this area come to be? Many thought the area detracted from the town's quaint lakeside appeal, but, of course, they didn't know the history. Heaven had been an industrial town first. Lake Michigan is merely an asset for commerce.

That ninth grade summer was a bundle of planning: car pools, driver's training, and practices. Sadie and Lisa would ride together to school. Billy was almost driving, but went early because of early football practice. The girls would arrive just in time to sit on the window ledge of the floor to ceiling windows and watch all the kids go by. Everyone had their own "reserved" spots on "the ledge" that went the full length of the school. Laughter and good morning cheers lived alongside bullying hate looks and whispers. Young lovers would steal kisses and feels, and those not in any "in" crowd would lap the hallways in a never ending walking pattern.

One morning, Lisa had to walk down to the gym locker room. Miss Aitch, the Girl's Phys. Ed. teacher had a form that needed to be signed and turned in by the first bell. Even though this was her first hour class, Lisa wanted to make sure she was following the directions to the letter. She headed there as soon as she visited her locker. There was a good 15 minutes until the first bell.

She never went down by the gymnasium before school. It felt like an alien planet. No one walked down that hall and there was no window ledge. Lights were on half power. It was dim. The steel grate that closed off the entry doors to the ticket office and pool area was still in place. Lisa reached for the door of the locker room.

"You're that cheerleader, aren't you?' Someone murmured from the stairs that led to the pool bleachers. Even though the pool was closed, there was no grate in front of the first five or so stairs. Lisa looked up. The stairs were filled with black students. Mainly freshmen and sophomores. All girls. They hadn't made a sound as she approached. They sat in the dark and as her eyes adjusted she counted 12 or more girls.

Lisa gave a tight smile. No teeth. She was a little frightened.

"Well are you?" Someone else asked.

The air felt thick. If she hadn't been holding onto the door handle, she would have turned and booked down the other way.

She saw a girl squatting down to see better.

"Oh. That's Lisa Palma! You know. Her brother is Billy."

"Uh huh." Someone else said, "He sure is fine."

There were nods of agreement as Lisa moved and opened the door of the locker room. She had been saved by someone she didn't even know. For once she was thankful for Billy.

She dropped the form on Miss Aitch's desk. Miss Aitch looked up and saw that Lisa was breathing quickly.

"Lisa. You know, when I first started working here I was fresh out of a North Carolina college. Those girls intimidated me in the beginning. But they are just as frightened as you are. Just act naturally."

Miss Aitch! I wonder how she knew I was scared. Lisa thought. How does she think we are alike?

Lisa scrutinized her thin figure in the gym teacher outfit. She looked like a model right out of a magazine. Or an actress. Her café-au-lait skin was smooth, her hair straight with signs of curls up near her part. She had confidence and talked to everyone the same way. But she was a teacher and she was African American.

"But I thought that area was off limits." Lisa said, "You know, the pool steps."

"Where else are they going to go?" Miss Aitch got a little testy then. "You going to make room on the ledge for them?"

"I could. I mean…I just didn't know…" Lisa was at a loss.

"You are a nice girl. But there are a lot of things you don't know. Open your eyes. This is one small town in Michigan but it could be any town in North Carolina. I will talk to you anytime you want to about things you don't know. But don't be getting all self-righteous with the fact that the black girls have a place to go and the rules aren't the same. They aren't. It's lopsided."

"Okay, Miss Aitch, how come there aren't black kids on the ledge in the morning? Why try to be so different? They could sit on the ledge. It belongs to everyone. No one would yell at them or make them move. This is not the only place they have to go. They are trying to be separate. You let that happen. Even here in the locker room they sit up where the baskets are. Every girl has to go through that group to get a basket and they get harassed. Some girls don't even use those baskets for clothes but go through the hassle of bringing them home every day so they can avoid confrontation. Why don't you do something about that? Why do I have to be yelled at and confronted to answer to people who are not even trying to be my friend? They try to intimidate. I don't think that is any way to treat anyone. I don't do that to them. I just came here to bring you my permission slip and they were all over me. How is that even fair?"

"It's fair because life's not fair. What do you do to let them know you want to be their friends, huh? Do you say, "Join me on the ledge?" Sure, you don't confront, but isn't it the same to silently ignore? Do you see their intimidation as a cry to be visible? Because you should. And if you can't figure that out, well, you are part of the problem. Now scoot out of here. The bell's going to ring any second."

When Lisa walked out of the locker room she felt scolded. Hell, she didn't do anything. She was grateful that that Lynn girl had diffused the group, but that Jill Turner was a girl to avoid. She knew exactly how it felt to be invisible. She knew why she fought so hard to be noticed. She knew about validation. This was sure a heavy thing to think at this time in the morning. She would need time to shed light on her personal dark corners. But she would stay away from any threat until then.

Hurrying down the hallway, she felt the books slipping out of her arms. They fell all at once, but no one stopped their frenzied pace to help. Except one. She heard him first.

"I knew we'd meet again."

She looked up. It was the boy from the beach. The one who had helped her the day of the fight between neighborhoods. He was leaning down to pick up her books.

"Remember me? Jed Adams? Walk you to class?"

Lynn

Lynn rushed into her room after school. She was going to get homework done right away so she could go flirt around down at Moon Park. It was already October and she was pulling down good grades in all her subjects.

She heard rustling around in the kitchen, and voices. Male voices. Old male voices. William had his "newest friend" Gilbert over for a few glasses of wine. Lynn didn't like Gilbert. He looked at her too long and smacked his lips after she went by like it was a joke. She knew to stay in her room until after he left. She worked on her Algebra equations and was just closing the book when her door opened.

"Hello, Miss Lynn," She heard.

"Gilbert, get out of my room, please." She said nicely.

"My, but you do keep a tidy room." Gilbert continued, making no effort to leave.

"I asked you nicely, now I am going to call Lamar." Lynn felt cornered.

Gilbert started touching his fingers lightly over her bed and up her pillow. He said,

"He ain't here Lynn. Just left. Said something about football practice." He picked her pillow up and put his face in it breathing deeply.

"Then I need to start supper before Mama comes home." Lynn's voice had an edge in it. "If you touch anything else in here I will scream!"

"Mama's got a meeting. William sent me to tell you that I will be your guest for dinner tonight." Gilbert had moved up behind Lynn's chair. She shot out of it, pushing him back.

"If you don't get out of here, I am going to tell my mama that you came in my room and would not leave. I know your kind, you old, stinky mother fucker." Lynn was lit now. This old man was looking her over like a show horse. "I will break you in two." She said hotly, "Just push me and you aren't going to know what hit you."

"Ho! Ho! Such a nasty mouth!" He cried. "This time I will go, but next time we are going to put that big luscious mouth to use." He licked his chops and rubbed the zipper of his pants.

When the door closed, Lynn burst into tears. It seemed like she was constantly fending off the men her stepfather brought home. With her mother called away for meetings more and more, Lynn was going to need to come up with a plan that would take her out of the house as much as possible. But her mother wanted her to cook dinner. She made up her mind to prep meals a few days in advance so that they could be put together quickly.

That night, she put a placemat out for her mother as she did every evening. She decided not to prepare a place for Gilbert Morse, since Mama didn't like him hanging around. She put the chicken on the table, the greens were still hot on the stove, and there was a basket of biscuits with butter and Grandpa's honey. She changed her clothes and put on her huge "everything's okay with Lynn" smile, then promptly turned around and ran out the door to Diann's and the park.

Lisa

Jed Adams was smiling at her when she placed her books in her locker after class.

"Now that I know where your locker is, I can make sure you won't have any other problems with your books," he said.

Lisa tried to avoid looking into those deep blue eyes. They were like sapphires with many layers of depth and they were hypnotizing her. She looked away thinking: Oh, this would never work out. Having any kind of relationship with a boy tied to Baver Court was a recipe for disaster. Her dad would forbid it and her brother would likely take any opportunity to rough the kid up. She needed to push him back out of her thoughts.

"I am perfectly fine, now. But thanks. I appreciate your help this morning." She knew it was a rebuff and tried hard for it not to sound too bitchy.

"Well, since I have saved you a few times, how about if I give you a ride home. You don't want to walk through the Zone by yourself." Jed was practically pushing her out the door to the parking lot.

She looked around. There were teams practicing and since she had practice in the morning, there was no excuse. She knew

Jed played football and the second practice would be around 5 PM. She decided to take a calculated risk and got in the car. After all, she could make a friend in him, couldn't she?

With windows down, Jed turned the radio on. It wasn't super hard rock, like most of the kids were saying they loved, but Chicago, with lots of horns and instruments. She began to relax a little.

"Should we take a quick pass down the north beach?" he asked, his face hopeful.

"I really have to get home, Lisa said, "My mom is expecting me."

"No problem," Jed answered as he put the car in gear, humming along with the music.

He was so self-assured. She was used to boys being nervous around her.

As they approached the stop sign, he took a right turn.

"Wait. You know I live on Apache, right?" Lisa asked with a little laugh.

"You say you don't want to cruise the beach with your words, but your eyes say otherwise," He said smiling.

Hmm. Lisa thought. This pisses me off a little bit. I know he is trying to show me off in his car to the gang that hangs out at the beach after school. No. It pissed her off a lot.

"Umm. Jed?" She asked. "Please pull over."

Thinking she dropped something, Jed pulled to the curb.

Lisa quickly got out and slammed the door. Jumping to the sidewalk, she looked over and said,

"Thanks for the ride."

Jed just sat in the car. He didn't attempt to chase her. He watched her walk toward Lakeshore Blvd.

Lisa never looked back. She was thinking it was a kind of creepy power play. She didn't like his pushy style. 'No' was supposed to mean 'no'. She vowed never to get caught up in something like this again.

The next day, she breathed a sigh of relief when he wasn't at her locker before school. In fact, she didn't see him most of the day. She was beginning to second guess her decision to be the strong feminist, after all, it was just a ride around the beach. But she knew that she was being used like a trophy to show off, and she wasn't ready to explain why she was hanging around with this guy in the first place.

When the last bell rang, she closed her locker in time to see Jed. He was hanging out near the steps, watching her.

She waved and smiled as if to say 'no hard feelings'.

He turned and walked out the door.

Oh, no! She thought. I have really blown it with him.

Without thinking it over, she ran to the door. He was sitting on the bench in front of the school talking to Sadie. Just what she didn't need. She began to walk by when Sadie called out,

"Hey Lisa! Jed is coming over to my house. You want to come too?"

"Okay," Lisa replied a little too quickly. Had they just conspired or did Sadie have an interest in this super cute sophomore?

They got in the car. Sadie scooted over to the middle of the front seat next to Jed, and Lisa got in beside her. They took the long route around the north beach. Jed honked and waved to the gang of teenagers hanging out at the beach parking lot. Since he was with the girls, they were greeted with shouts from the growing beach crowd. Some were yelling to stop and others were merely scratching their heads. Jed was new to school this year. A lot of the girls had already been checking him out.

"You sure know a lot of people," Sadie said to Jed.

"Oh, TJ and Andy are my stepbrothers." Jed explained.

"So your full name is Jed Adams. I wasn't sure because when I looked you up in the class roster for study hall, it listed you by a different name," Sadie said laughingly.

"My mom married TJ and Andy's dad. He has been really slow in getting my adoption stuff in. I will be changing my name for real whenever it's finalized. My real name is Jed Forter."

"You sound like you're not sure it's going to happen,." Lisa stated "Is your dad from around here?"

"Nope," Jed said "He and my mom lived here for a while with his folks. But the piece of shit knocked my mom around a lot. Didn't pay support. She had to get so many restraining orders. She met Vic because he worked at the court. My dad had to go to jail for a few months and my mom filed for divorce. Haven't seen my old man since. We are better off with Vic...well she is."

The car was quiet. Lisa asked to be dropped off at the top of the hill leading down to the dead ended street. Her father would not have been happy with her riding around. His rule was to come straight home from school or practice. She told Sadie and Jed to give her about 15 minutes before she came over. Sadie wiggled her fingers goodbye but her head was still turned to Jed. They took off to make another beach run.

The twins were practicing piano when she opened the door. They were the only ones with even the remotest interest in music. There were shoes and bookbags all over. Carla, Lisa's mother, was busily putting the last touches on a roast. They ate promptly at 6 PM and dinner would be perfectly done by then.

The phone was ringing.

"Leave us alone!" Her mother yelled.

Just another day in paradise, Lisa thought, reaching for the wall phone situated in the kitchen.

"Palma residence," She said as she answered.

"Lisa, it's Lynn. Lynn Parris from school."

"Hey Lynn. What's up?"

"I was talking to Ms. Aitch and she says you and I should be in charge of intramural sports for freshmen girls this winter at school."

"Okay, but it's only October," Lisa said. "What's her rush?"

"Well, I think there are others pressuring her to give up her key, and she wants girls she can trust."

"Well, I wonder how I can do cheerleading practice and do intramurals," Lisa said.

"Ms. Aitch told me you'd say that," Lynn laughed. "She said to tell you it's Monday nights for freshmen girls, the day you don't have practice."

"Ha! That works for me, then."

"Me too!" Lynn said happily. "I figure we will offer volleyball first and then see if anyone wants to use the basketball nets. If we can leave those up then we can have five or six games of volleyball at once."

"Do we have to have referees? I heard girls really fight when a bad call is made."

"Let's see what Ms. Aitch says," Lynn said. "She is going to be glad we said yes."

"Sounds like a plan, Lynn!" Lisa said, getting ready to hang up.

"By the way, Lisa. I saw who you got a ride home with today," Lynn began. "Looked like Sadie Ryan was sitting on his lap! If I were you, I might think about going after that man."

Sadie Ryan was practically on his lap, thought Lisa. If I don't make an effort to let him know I like him, she will certainly go after him.

"He's cute," Lynn finished.

"Lynn," Lisa decided to confide in her new friend "do you think a person can overcome a bad past? I mean, all the movies you see about child abuse and stuff? I feel like Jed has had a tough life."

"I am honored that you asked me that question, Lisa," Lynn said. "My people have been overcoming bad pasts for generations. I think there are scars left that are hard to overcome, but the best way to know if hardships can be overcome is if they get a fair shake at life. And they need to have a sense of humor."

"Thanks for giving me that," Lisa said. "Wondering what makes people tick, sometimes."

"I hear you, Lisa," Lynn said, "But you never know unless you take a chance."

After ending the conversation, Lisa knew Lynn would be a

safe confidante. She couldn't share too much with anyone else as it would surely make it back to her parents. Lynn's advice was sound and she had the "cover of darkness"; two things Lisa needed most.

The following day, she took the ride offered by Jed and suggested they go up the coast to Glenn. Her parents thought she was going over to a friend's house to study and Jed never seemed to have much to do now that football was over. There was a bite to the fall air, but climbing out on the clay cliffs high above the water presented an epic view. They lounged around in the sand, put their feet in freezing water, and did a little chit chatting.

Jed was so good looking. The fact that he was becoming a popular kid, seemed to offset his background of a broken home. He was beginning to appeal to her. After some time out on the cliffs, they decided it would be best if he took her home. She said that maybe he should drive her all the way home so her parents got used to seeing her in the car.

From then on, the afterschool spots became more varied and fun. Soon, they were bringing snacks and blankets and it was becoming apparent that they were forming a partnership at school too.

After Lisa came home one afternoon, in time for dinner, her brother Billy, brought up the fact that she was spending so much time with Jed Adams.

"He's a nice kid," Lisa said. "We aren't doing anything wrong."

"He has family on Baver Court," Billy said. "Those hicks are the same blood as he is."

Lisa's dad chimed in: "You are to come home every night

after school, young lady. No more joy rides with this guy. Billy will bring you home."

Billy was crestfallen. Now, he couldn't do his secret rendezvous with his girlfriend after school. He gave Lisa a hateful stare. Thanks a lot. His eyes flashed.

Lisa knew better than to complain. She simply didn't speak. That night after dinner, she called Lynn to help her with a plan for meeting up with Jed.

Lynn

School and its activities had taken a lot of her attention away from Gilbert Morse. Lynn knew he had been there at the house during the day from all the empty cans and bottles strewn around. She picked one up to find it filled with cigarette butts floating like so many drowned fish.

She didn't mind cleaning it up, though. As long as the house was empty, she could tidy up and start dinner without her mother being the wiser. She knew that, in a way, she was helping William's aimless nature. Her stepfather had not worked in ages, except for the bar on weekends. She suspected he had many side hustles going on. It seemed like her mother was just tolerating him now. They had really quarreled about the disability checks and strangers in the house. Mama said that Gilbert was up to no good, and if William chose to lounge around with someone during the day instead of getting a job, he might as well pack up his things.

Compiling a meatloaf, she got it into a pan and slid it into the oven. Her new plan to prepare things in advance was working. It was something her grandmother would have done. Her goal was to keep practicing so she could be just like her someday.

The potatoes were in a pan of water and as it heated she went upstairs to quickly change clothes. The door was open and there was a rummaging sound coming from her bedroom.

Frightened, because the kids were downstairs, she grabbed a bottle from the trash, and pushed her door in quickly. Gilbert Morse was on her bed and he was drunk as a skunk. In his fumbling around to find the toilet, he'd completely missed the bathroom and stumbled into Lynn's room. The puddle in the corner reeked to high heaven.

"You better get out of here right now," Lynn said with a shaky voice. Gilbert was one of those mean drunks.

"Well, well. If it isn't my fine piece," He said, his eyes clouded with lust. "Come on over here. I got something to teach you with."

Lynn was stricken as she watched him take off his pants. There was no hiding what he wanted to do. Things began moving in slow motion. Lynn turned to leave but she underestimated Gilbert's strength. He was a wiry kind of strong and he pulled Lynn down on the bed, the bed that her grandfather made for her as a birthday present long ago. The cheap wine she smelled on his breath let her know that there was no way to talk sense to him. But she needed help. She opened her mouth to scream. He clasped his hand over her mouth and dug a pair of socks out of her open dresser drawer. Prying her mouth as wide as he could, he jammed the socks in and kept pushing. Finally, he flipped her on her stomach and pushed her denim skirt all the way up to her waist.

"Oh, I'ma teach you good, little girl. You sneering at me like I'm trash."

Lynn's face was smashed in the pillow as Gilbert forcibly took her. In an instant, she turned from a young maiden into a marginalized, damaged woman.

It was over quickly. Lynn kept her head down and stayed quiet.

Gilbert was looking at her with a glint in his eye.

"My, my!" He said, "this is the beginning of a beautiful relationship."

Lynn looked up at him and said,

"If you ever come into this house again, I will kill you."

The front door opened. They both heard it. By the sounds of the heavy footsteps, they knew it was William. After charging up the stairs, he knocked on Lynn's door. Gilbert opened it.

William took one look at Lynn's compromised position on the bed and said to Gilbert:

"Now, why'n ya gotta do that for? Haven't I been getting you all the little girl tail that you wanted? I told you not to mess with Zenobia's children. Get out of here. You have created a problem. You get that, right? Find somewhere to sleep it off, man. Don't come back here."

Gilbert put a hand through his hair and showed signs that he was sobering up. He left without a word.

"Lynn," William began, "he said he would leave you girls alone. You know, he is a drunk and when he gets so much alcohol, or drugs, for that matter, he loses his head. I won't have him here again, Lynn. But you can't tell your mama what just happened. She doesn't understand what the addicted mind does. I will run his ass out of town. That's what I'll do. Just so we're clear. I would hate to have to physically make my point with you, you understand."

Lynn stood and fixed her clothes. Her bedding was a mess. There was piss in the corner. This haven - her only refuge- was sullied by this event. Now, as if to smooth things over, William was peeling dollar bills out of a wallet filled with money. He put $40 on the dresser and turned around to go. Lynn was motionless in the middle of her room. She hadn't said a word through his excuses. She guessed she was in shock.

So many things were flashing through her head.

Rape. Can't tell Mama. Finally know how that all works. Money from William. Just like a prostitute.

"You touch a hair on my head, you hateful black devil, and I will make sure you rot in jail." They were her first words. Spoken low in barely a whisper, they were forceful. "I expect I can keep quiet for $50 a week. You know my momma would see through you faster than a moth eaten horse tick. Now, how does my side hustle sound to you?"

William's eyes opened wide. For the first time he was feeling his power over Lynn draining.

"Lynn. You know I ain't got that kind of money," he said.

"I believe you will have to come up with some new side hustle of your own then, William. You sure ain't sharing that wad of money there with my mother. Your homeless ass will be on the street with your drunk, criminal friend. I am 15 years old, William. Fifteen!" Lynn was trying to stop her emotions. "Mama is going to be here any minute and you need to be gone. I can't trust myself to not say something to her."

"Well, well, well," he said clicking his teeth and shaking his head. "Look who is all high and mighty now?" He moved down the steps as if he said some earth shattering exit line. Lynn heard the door slam.

She quickly went downstairs and locked it. Getting a glass of water, she sat at the kitchen table. The kids were watching television in the other room during her minutes of horror. They were protected from a kind of trauma they would learn about soon enough. Folding her arms on the table, she lay her head down and cried silently.

It was worse than a robbery. Her whole life she would see Gilbert Morse stuffing her mouth with a sock and pushing her on the bed. This was not the way it should have been. Her girlfriends constantly talked about finding their first love. How could she even enter the conversation? She was ruined at 15 years old, in a matter of minutes. Damaged goods that could never be put back together.

She allowed herself ten minutes of self-pity. These feelings needed to be packed away for another time. Her mother would be home from work soon and dinner needed to be finished. Stuffing down the depth of what had happened, she reached inside her soul and dragged out the face with the dazzling smile. This is who Mama would see when she came home. After mashing the potatoes, she set the table for dinner. She exhaled out her lips in a few long breaths. There was talking outside followed by Mama coming in the door.

"Girl," Lynn told herself, "you have got to keep it together."

"Your meatloaf smells delicious, Lynn. Just like my mother's,"

Zenobia remarked as she put her coat up on the peg.

"Hi Mama. You are just in time."

William pushed in behind her mother. It looked as if he had composed himself from the day-long drinking spree. Lynn looked at him, and her eyes appraised what was obviously supposed to be some sort of contrition for the terrible deed done to her. His act would not get past her mother. She would feel something was up.

"I am sorry I won't be able to eat here tonight," William said with a jolly tone. "I have a little something I have to do."

"Harumph," Zenobia looked at him with eyes that had watched all the possibilities of a good life go running through her hands like sand. "It must be nice to sleep whenever you want, eat food you don't pay for, run around with crazy drunken fools. I am getting to my last straw with you."

It was a warning, Lynn knew.

Mama went to change her clothes and William handed Lynn a fifty dollar bill. He put his finger up to his mouth for her to be silent. Lynn couldn't even look at him. She pocketed the money and continued to set the table.

"And not even a thank you?" William said.

"You need to beat ass out of here or Lamar is going to be told. He doesn't need much of an excuse to mess you up. And the minute you don't put money in my hand for what happened here today, will be your last moment under this roof. Mama will kick you out on your sorry behind."

The screen door banged as William took the stairs two at a time.

Lynn felt powerful. For the moment, she felt like everything was in her control.

Lisa

Things with Jed had become confusing. Ever since they had decided to have an exclusive boyfriend–girlfriend relationship. His moods were a roller coaster that went from happy and easy going to dark and hostile in a heartbeat. A few times in the last few months, he started an argument. It usually had to do with other boys that were talking to Lisa. He told her that she was not to talk or laugh with anyone else or he would break up with her. She felt special with someone being so jealous about having her all to himself. At first, it was kind of cute. But lately, there was more and more shouting than smiling.

She had jumped into the relationship eagerly. She fought her dad tooth and nail until he conceded that it was okay for her to go to the Christmas Dance with him. She was ecstatic and she and Sadie planned how to style her hair and what dress to wear.

Seeing Lynn in the hall, Lisa went up to her to show her pictures of the dance. Lynn, who had decided not to go, was actually a little cold to Lisa. After Lisa and Jed had announced themselves a couple at the high school dance in the fall, Lynn was less and less supportive of her relationship with Jed.

She didn't like that Lisa pretended to like sitting by herself until her boyfriend came into school. It was humiliating to her. The way she waited for him head down was beginning to look like a little trained dog. When they sat together on the ledge and watched people go by Jed watched Lisa to see if she smiled at anyone. She pushed out her girlfriends for him and was missing the best part of high school, Lynn thought. Though many stopped to say hello to Jed, Lisa just smiled. Jed told her that he preferred to do the talking and she shouldn't even greet people unless he said it was okay.

Lisa knew that Lynn was very angry with her for quitting cheerleading. Lynn told her that she shouldn't stop doing what she loved just because her boyfriend didn't want her to. They hadn't spoken for weeks afterward. Lisa was mad at Lynn's judgmental stance, mainly because it was closer to the truth than she knew.

What actually had happened was in doing a flip-turn, Lisa's skirt had also flipped and all the audience could see was a brief glimpse of the uniform bottoms that were worn under the skirt for just those occasions. Jed went around to the hallway door and asked Lisa to come out. It was during the first quarter of the basketball game, so the only people in the hall were concession stand workers and their patrons. It would fill up until half time. Jed pushed her around a corner where they would be hidden and slammed her hard against the wall by the shoulders. Her head hit the wall and she saw stars.

"Do you know that EVERYONE in the stands saw your panties just now? Everyone! You are quitting this stupid thing. You look like a hoe."

"Jed," Lisa had said soothingly, "that's part of our uniform. Don't be silly."

He took some skin just above her elbow and squeezed it between his thumb and forefinger. The pain was excruciating. There were several other small bruises near that spot from previous scolding. He really knew how to place his abuse.

"I said you will quit or we will be through. Got it?"

"Okay. But I have got to finish this game." She managed. She watched him lope out the door into the chilly winter night.

Lisa quickly looked around. She learned that crying only made people more concerned so she bottled up the embarrassment. How was she going to pull this off? Her school only allowed girls one sport a season and this season her sport was cheerleading.

Thankfully, that little encounter hadn't been seen. She shook her head. She would think about it later. But when she turned she had come face-to- face with Lynn.

"Lisa," Lynn said. "Why do you let that boy treat you like that? Do you think people don't know what's going on?" She gestured to the stands. "I saw him through the door. Pacing and ugly. You don't think there are others that don't know how he treats you?"

"I know he's got good inside. I love him, Lynn." She replied lamely.

"That's a lot of things, but it isn't love." Lynn said, "Girl, you have bruises all over your arms. Do you think you are hiding that? He may be cute, but there is something very wrong with that boy."

"Lynn, I can't break up with him. He says he will jump off the pier if I do."

"He's going to do you harm. What would your father say? Or your brother?"

"They can't know, Lynn. They think it is okay right now."

"Is that right?" She said as if she was a parent herself. "Lisa, your brother was inquiring in the Zone about possible gangs that might rough someone up real bad. I don't know if he was just talking shit to Lamar, but he sure wanted to know about gangs and what they can do. He seemed to be placing a lot of interest on Jed and his family. He really doesn't like him."

"But Lynn, right now, there is no way out of this. Every time I turn around, Jed is watching. You know, Mr. Shwill took me out of class the other day. He brought the guidance counselor with him. They said I needed to get away from this 'toxic' relationship. Shwill is threatening to call my father. I know my dad. He will break Jed's face or worse!"

Head Cheerleader Caryn ran out into the hall.

"Lisa, are you okay? We are on for halftime."

"Okay."

Lynn said,

"Let's talk this weekend,"

Lisa thought that had an ominous ring to it so she avoided all of Lynn's calls. Finally, Lynn gave up.

It left Lisa and Jed. Sadie was out a long time ago, hoping to not get in the middle of any bad feelings.

But Lisa was having second thoughts too. Things were getting physical. She firmly told Jed 'no' to any form of lovemaking that involved sex all the way. He was pressuring her and when she refused, he was hurting her. Today, seeing Lynn in the hall, made her miss her friend.

I need to get out and I am probably going to need help.

She decided to make a plan to confront Jed.

After babysitting on Saturday, Lisa asked to go out with Jed. He rode a bike over to her regular Saturday morning babysitting job for Barbara McGrath. Barbara had a standing appointment at the Marinella Salon for a hair styling. Lisa saw him come around the corner of the subdivision, his black ringlets catching and reflecting the sun, his blue eyes smiling.

He asked her what she had in mind for later and she simply said we need to talk. No matter how much he pinched, slapped, punched or shoved, it would be hard for her to cut ties with this totally handsome, white-toothed, smiling teenage boy. He left as quickly as he came, telling her he'd pick her up in his car. He was on cloud nine. They were a happy couple again.

When Barbara got home from the beauty parlor, her hair stiff and immobile with hairspray and a new brown barrette affixed to the center of her hairdo, she noticed an old bruise on Lisa's arm. It had been several weeks since that argument with Jed and the bruise had a green cast to it now.

"I certainly hope you had an accident" Mrs. M. said in a very matter-of-fact way. "If you did, I am sorry. If you didn't, knowing your father, I am even sorrier."

"What are you saying?" Lisa giggled, "I am not an idiot."

"Just a fool for love, like the song?" Mrs. McGrath was not letting up.

"I appreciate your concern but I am really fine."

"You can always talk to me, if you aren't okay," Barbara said

"Thanks, I guess." Lisa got out of McGrath's car and she was boiling mad. That lady had a lot of gall to assume something was up because she had a small bruise.

An hour passed and she appreciated the familiar ease as Jed's car approached. It made her almost excited. He honked instead of coming to the door, her dad's pet peeve, but her dad wasn't there so she ran out the door. She was hopeful for a fun couple of hours, hoping she wouldn't set off any triggers. She saved the real talking part until later.

They headed to the tennis courts to play a few easy sets of tennis. Jed was a good player. He taught Lisa a few good strategies and she wondered where he had ever taken lessons. He told her that he watched a lot of tennis on television and was able to pick up most of it there.

Lisa thought the afternoon was going well. He won with a score of 6-3, 7-5. She worried the last set was a little too close for his ego. She had a right to be worried. She noticed Jed's face had a distant look when he got in the car. Lisa was ignoring his mood, hoping it would pass. They shut the doors and Lisa turned her head to ask him if something was the matter.

The slap came out of nowhere but with the force of a well-developed forehand. It turned her head around.

"I am never playing with you again, you bitch!" Jed cried, "You cheated through the entire game, calling balls out that were

SO IN! It's no goddam fun to play with a cheater!"

Lisa was blindsided. Her head hit the window so hard she could feel a bump emerging. It sounded like a ripe melon or red rubber playground ball being slammed against the car. Tears began sliding out of the corners of her eyes. She must have deserved this, she thought. How am I going to have a talk with him now? She stuffed down the shame and let it sit in the closed up place in her heart. She was learning that if she cried hard, when he was pummeling her, it would only rev him up more. This wasn't the first time this had happened. But it was the first time she felt trapped. She didn't want him in her life anymore.

She got mad. Yelling, screaming and attacking him back turned her into a punching bag. With each blow she quieted as she was jerked this way or that, with new cuts opening and old ones changing color. She learned that she could put herself somewhere else and watch the beatings, as if they were happening to someone else. With his rage spent, and likely his own hands aching, he mopped his brow and ended it.

Today, she crawled deep inside herself. Unable to speak, she kept her head down and let her wounds bleed freely.

"You are going straight home. Forget any food or something to drink," He muttered as he started up the car. "I am out with my buddies tonight and if I so much as sniff you out of your house, you will wish you'd never been born!"

Lisa knew this whole thing was messed up. She didn't do one thing. She simply sat. Her gut clenched from the body blows and now she was nauseated from swallowing blood from her nose.

She knew she was a mess. She needed out. There was no one to talk to.

At the top of her street, Jed demanded a kiss goodbye. She gingerly kissed him with her bloody lip. "Ugh," he said. "You got blood and shit all over me." He pulled the rearview mirror down and checked for any blood smears.

"Well, get out," he said as if he was talking to someone four years old.

She walked, as a zombie, past several houses, with her tennis shorts spotted with blood and hair matted and messy. She was so grateful that the garage door was open. The shower room was open and she quickly took a shower and put on a fresh tee shirt and shorts. She felt a pang as she stuck the blood soaked tennis sweater, her favorite tennis item ever, into a shopping bag and hid it deep inside the garbage can. Nothing was going her way. I hate him and I love him. How can that even be right? He was tearing her in two, both mentally and physically.

She needed to talk to Lynn. She had become her only confidante, since the situation was way too embarrassing to relay to her "regular" friends. Lynn knew what it was like to have flawed men who took their anger out on their women. Lisa felt like Lynn really understood.

Lisa needed advice.

She was happy to have a breather from him. She called Lynn's house but she was spending the night at her grandmother's house. Lisa took stock of her face and thought she could cover up the bruises with peach pancake makeup she ripped off from the high school theater department. Her resolve was stronger now. I have to get out of this.

That night, she turned the television on for noise. There was a documentary on Jimi Hendrix's addiction to heroin. How gradually it took him over and ruined him in so many ways, Lisa felt her relationship with Jed was, in some ways, a kind of addiction. She loved him so much when he was light and sweet. He made her feel like a princess. But there was always payment. The harmony didn't last.

The next day, after church, the phone rang. Jed wanted to apologize for being so "rough". He had an hour or two to waste and thought he would see if she could come out. Lisa tried everything she could think of to not have to be with him but he seemed really full of contrition. Finally, she agreed on a 45 minute window of time. She said the younger kids were home and her mother expected her back early to watch them. She couldn't go far.

They rode to the beach and got out and watched the waves. Jed laughed and tried to cuddle on a blanket he put out on the sand. No one would ever have guessed that he was beating her up in broad daylight just the day before. She was standoffish. He knew he had crossed a line and he gently touched her swollen face and kissed each wound. It was time to go, Lisa thought.

"Jed, it's time for me to head home," she said. "I have been gone for over an hour."

They got in the car. Jed said, "Oh man. Lee and I scored the best weed last night."

She made one comment about weed being illegal and was actually trying to tell him to be smart about it, when before she knew it, she became a punching bag again.

Her nose began to bleed immediately and she rummaged around in her purse for a tissue. Over the past few months she was learning what moves to make to help him calm down. She recognized that the gritting of his teeth (they weren't as nice as his eyes, and crooked on the bottom) and the balling of his fists, were signs that he was revving up into some kind of fit. But she really couldn't tell if he was going to slap, pinch, grab, or punch.

Normally, the best thing to do was to take it, but she was still hurting from the night before. She put her hands up to fend him off.

"Oh this is something new," he chuckled. But he stopped swinging.

He put the car in drive and took her straight home. He stopped in front of the driveway. Great. Her parents were looking out the window. Somehow, she had to go into the house, with blood seeping down her nose. But, she was becoming a pro at it. She waited for Jed to say something. Apologize? Good bye?

The longer they waited, the more likely her parents would ask questions. She opened the door and got out. Jed took off so quickly, his car rolled right over her foot. She was stunned temporarily by the numb pain and then tried to run into the house, horrified. He knew what he had done because after he turned around to go back, he yelled out the window,

"You sure have big feet!"

Opening the screen door, she hobbled past her parents saying quickly,

"I have to pee like a racehorse."

Her mother asked what was wrong with her foot.

"Must have rolled it when I played tennis yesterday." she said.

She stocked the freezer with wet washcloths put in bags to place on sore "tennis muscles." She grabbed one on the way to the bathroom, where she spent the next few tedious minutes stopping the blood, stifling the swell, and applying frozen washcloth after frozen washcloth. This was her second time "cleaning up" in two days and things were getting harder and harder to hide.

That night, she made up her mind. She really did not love the guy at all. Breaking up with him made her feel like a failure. She had to figure this out because one of these times, he was going to go too far. She had to get out.

But the next day, he was calling her again. He was contrite.

"Lisa, I am so sorry that happened. I just lose my head when someone tells me I am no good or doing something illegal. I will try harder."

Lisa didn't even beg the question by saying that she hadn't really said that at all. She just paused and let him continue about how sorry he was because she knew there was something else he wanted to ask.

"Can you go out climbing the cliffs today? I will make you a beautiful picnic and make up for the asshole I have been."

"Maybe we need a breather, Jed, "Lisa began "I have homework and am not okay with the stuff that happened yesterday."

He cried then. Long howling sobs like a wounded dog.

"I am so sorry. I promise…" He was talking through so much

snot and tears that she finally agreed to go for a little while. He was melting down. Lisa realized she was going to have to break it off with him in stages.

"If you ever broke up with me, I would jump off the pier and drown myself. Or worse, I would mess myself up real bad and have you be the one to find me," he said. "Can I pick you up at 1:00 PM? Okay? Please? Please say yes?"

Lisa felt herself caving again. She looked in the mirror. Various places on her face were covered with so much makeup it was causing breakouts. Her eyes were sunken and had circles from the pain in her foot. Although initially it gave her pain, she iced it and elevated it most of the night, and today it felt better.

She needed to make a way to break up without retribution. She put another time frame on it. "I can go from 12:30-2:00 PM," she told him, "but that will be pushing it. We really need to talk."

"However much time I can get with you", he crooned.

And just like that it was all erased for him.

But not entirely for her. Each time something happened, Lisa wrote about it in her journal. She wanted to be strong enough to just make the break. She would not leave out any details. She went to it now. Since she began being his girlfriend, there were over 37 entries of abuse. Some entries were about the mind games he'd played at first, then the slapping, and lately the punching. Running his car over her foot was the final straw.

That day at the clay cliffs was beautiful and Jed had found some lucky stones on the beach. They were made from tiny circles, former prehistoric fish vertebrae, and he put them on a

thread to make a necklace. Lisa thought this was cute and little
boyish, somehow. It made her feel like she was going to have to
let him down in easy to understand layers.

But the ride into town was fine until the green LTD went
by and honked. Jed looked at Lisa,

"Why did you wave at them? They were my friends?"

He reached out and took her by the hair. With each yank of
her hair, he emphasized his words:

"Don't. Talk. Or Wave. To ANY Other guys!"

The final word had him gathering up his strength. She knew
there was a blow of some significant force coming. As he reeled
back, he released her hair. Grabbing the door handle, which Jed
had not locked, she pulled and let the force of his blow push her
out onto the sidewalk. She sprang up to run. He put the car in
park, but was still running in the middle of the street, and went
to run after her.

"Not so fast, Jed."

Boom! He collided full tilt into a huge man with highly
toned muscles.

It was Jed's coach, and the father of one of the football players. He grabbed Jed under his arms and lifted him up so high in
the air, Lisa, who had stopped to watch, thought he might be
hanging him up like a scarecrow on one of the light posts. But
he lowered him to face level and pressed him up against the
brick wall behind the movie theater.

"Do you have ANY idea whose daughter that is?" Coach
snarled, "Do you know that you should never, EVER, hit a woman?"

He reached back and gave Jed one open handed slap in the

face. The force of the blow turned Jed's head and he started to bawl. Coach Frell dropped him then.

"How's it feel, huh? Beating on a young girl like you're entitled. Like she is a dog! I knew your father was bad news, but you had a chance. You are just as fucked-up as he is. You'd better **never** let me catch you even looking at her funny, or I swear to God, I will take your face OFF!"

Coach looked over at Lisa and said,

"You need to get away from this guy."

Then the man got in his car and left.

Lisa turned down the river walk where Jed couldn't take his car. She was petrified and humiliated and so frightened that her father would find out. She followed the coach's car with her eyes. It appeared he was headed home and not to Lisa's home. She didn't dare look behind her for fear Jed had decided to finish up on the other side of her face. This was the termination of their relationship, thanks to the football coach. She was done with him. He knew that now.

She kept looking over her shoulder. She imagined it would be that way for a while. But she felt lighter than air as she walked, head up and shoulders back, down her little street toward home.

Lynn

It was unsettling for Lynn to see her friend so demoralized. That was one thing about white girls; They had their shit tied up all tidy. They didn't know how to live a messy life.

Lynn's ability to bounce back from the rape had been bumpy. Her stepfather was still trying to convince her that Gilbert wasn't doing anything wrong because of his drunken state, but when he'd made that comment to Gilbert that day, "Aren't I getting you all the little girls and boys you want?" It struck an odd chord with her. What was he talking about?

How could he minimize what had happened to her with "we won't need to tell your mother?"

She had been stricken for weeks that she might become pregnant and actually sobbed with relief when her period showed up a day or two late.

Lynn went on a quest to find answers. She wanted William out for good and she had to show her mother the side of him she knew was there but she hadn't seen. He was keeping his distance but his things were beginning to be strewn around the place again. He was coming here when everyone was at work or school and who knew who was coming with him.

The first thing she did was just observe him. Usually William spent a few hours down at the park. Occasionally, someone–usually a man–would come up to him in a car. William would get in and they would go somewhere, and then about an hour or so would pass and he'd get dropped back off at the park. After this happened several times in a few weeks, Lynn made a plan to follow.

She waited to make her move. The town was small. She could easily trail someone on her bike and not be noticed but if they went out to the country, like by her grandparent's house, she would never be able to get out there in time to find out anything.

She didn't have to wait long. She took her chance when she saw William get into a car and sit and talk a bit at the curb. She went upstairs where she could clearly see the car. The windows were blackened, making it impossible to see inside. But she wrote down the outer details about it. It was a new model Cadillac and it was a dark red–no more like burgundy. It had an Illinois license plate: JEX289. She placed the notepad of information in her top dresser drawer and stood ready to grab her bike as soon as it pulled away. There were many stop signs in the Zone. It was not easy to speed down any of the streets and Lynn was pretty sure that was their purpose. But it allowed cars to roll slowly by the people playing basketball or needing services or products of one kind or another, and a deal could be made right there at the window side, like a carhop at the drive-in. The burgundy Cadillac was slowly heading down by an old warehouse everyone called the frame factory. She followed to where she saw them turn in.

The factory had been one of the first in Heaven. At the time, railroad tracks passed alongside to pick up freight as they meandered through with their engines burping thick black smoke. Now the train tracks were moved closer to major industrial areas, and the factory had long since moved to a newer building leaving this facility with an old, rusted 'FOR SALE' sign and all the trees festooned with KEEP OUT markers. The drive to the factory building was overgrown with crabgrass and weeds. Grasshoppers munched and spit tobacco juice as the land seemed to be ingesting the building. Looking at its dilapidated surroundings and thick chain that was placed over the entry to the place, Lynn was puzzled as to why William and a man in a burgundy Cadillac were even here.

"Why would you park here?" She muttered under her breath. Somehow, they moved the chain and proceeded all the way down by the loading dock, keeping the engine running. Any number of things could be going on in that car, she thought.

She surely wasn't expecting the factory door by the dock to open. She hid her bike on the knoll above the parking lot. It allowed her to take in the scene, and get out if she had to. She hit the dirt so hard when the door opened, it took her a few seconds to catch her breath.

You can't make this shit up, she thought to herself because there, on the loading dock, stood none other than Gilbert Morse, and he was greeting the car. He gave some sort of hand signal to the car and a black gentleman got out. William was getting out too. The Cadillac man had a little strut to his gait. And ooh, his clothing, right down to his shoes dripped with money. Lynn watched him as gold chains large enough to choke a cat swung loosely from side to side on his bare chest. His polyester paisley shirt was unbuttoned to reveal his well worked pecs and massive frame. It looked like he bore a ring on every single finger. His legs were long in his golden polyester suit with a matching jacket. A sharp feather adorned his hat and was the same color as the Cadillac. He wore black boots that zipped up the side and obviously were brand new or highly shined. On his face were shades trimmed in gold. Thick gold. Lynn watched with mouth agape. This dude was a player. She had never seen anyone like this in her small town of Heaven.

Her best guess was a drug dealer, since everyone knew Gilbert had added 'junkie' onto his old title of alcoholic. But those deals were usually made right at the park, with no one batting an eye. This guy was dressed like a pimp; his afro big and picked out but tidy. He had a chain that held his wallet in his pants. Lynn sensed something epic was happening.

Lost in her gawking assessment of the Cadillac man, she didn't see William go to the driver's side of the car. She pasted herself into the side of the tree lining the old beat up drive. Seems William was driving now and he was leaving. He had that look of someone with a lot of details on their mind. Even though his head swept from side to side he wasn't really seeing anything. He sped off. Lynn was still very afraid to be spotted. She looked up to see the man do the stroll, like on Soul Train, right over to where Gilbert was standing and they both went inside.

Lynn was intrigued now. She hated Gilbert Morse. She

thought he was gone, like William had promised. But she knew better than to believe that. They never really left.

She picked up her bike and was getting ready to pedal around the other side of the old factory when back came the burgundy caddy. Fearing the driver would see her, she let her bike carry her over on the side of the embankment into the ditch. She landed with a thud but was too interested in the car even to see if she had sustained injuries.

From her perch above the old warehouse, Lynn saw William and a girl get out of the car. She was maybe 12 and not from around Heaven. Lynn knew all the black girls that lived in town and many of them were friends of her sisters. The girl had on a pair of scooter shorts that looked like they were painted onto her behind, and her two small, braless points stuck out of the tee shirt that was obviously several sizes too small. Her hair was braided into cornrows on both sides of her head and each braid had several multicolored beads on them. A very time consuming, sophisticated hair style for one so young, Lynn thought. She wondered who had the time and money to put into that hair. Most of Lynn's friends wore naturals or afros. These were the days when her race was pushing forward for equality in all things. But what struck Lynn most was that this girl had a full face of makeup. Heavy and dark, it made her look just like a street walker...Wait? What? Actually, Lynn thought to herself, she looks exactly like some of the ladies that hung out on the street behind the projects. But they were older than this girl.

William was sweet talking to this child. She was walking with stops and starts. It was clear she was not sold on going into the frame factory. Or maybe she was going to the frame factory "to be sold?" Something bad was going down and Lynn remembered the last thing she heard William say to Gilbert. Something about "haven't I been getting you enough little girls?"

Everything was starting to fall in place.

"Come over here now," Lynn called to the girl. "Hello, William. Was that Gilbert Morse I just saw behind that old door?"

William's suave, sweet talking persona cracked. He looked stricken like he had seen a ghost. Lynn had power here, she knew it. This guy was not going to be at her house any longer. She would make sure to get Gilbert and William out of her life on the same afternoon!

"So what, is this your new side hustle? Girls, William? For sale? Is that what this is?"

Turning to the girl, Lynn asked, "Honey, what did he promise you? Money? Nice clothes? Where are you from?"

Before the girl could answer, Lynn felt the clang of an old tire iron breeze past her face. Lucky for her, it was not a direct hit. Gilbert had a shaky hand. He was hopped up on something and looked as crazy as a rabid dog. Lynn lifted herself up and held her bike as a shield.

"Gilbert Morse. You raped me, now you going to do something with this little girl? Good for no damn thing. What are you going to do, huh?" She grabbed onto the tire iron.

Looking over at the girl she said: "Run! Go right to the police. Take the tracks straight down there and ask them to send someone here."

The girl ran. She made it down the old railroad tracks and

soon was out of sight. Lynn wondered if there were any other girls in the factory.

Gilbert raised his hand again and was bringing down the tire iron, when thwack!! A new steel Jimmy Connors 300 tennis racket hit him alongside the jaw. His teeth wobbled in his mouth. The tire iron was strewn several feet away. His haze, which had begun long before with a spoon and a needle, intensified in his head. He couldn't believe how viciously he was being attacked. He closed his eyes and tried to numb himself mentally.

With her perfect form, just buffed at practice, Lisa eloquently changed from backhand to forehand. She was in the zone just as if she were hitting the ball across the net, her strokes monotonous. Each blow landing about the head with lethal precision. Lynn, out of danger now, sat up and watched in disbelief. Body fluids were flying everywhere. Snot, blood, and spittle were mixing with Lisa's sweat as she kept hammering point after point, grunting with the effort of each backswing. Gilbert was definitely down for the count. In fact, he was such a bloody mess that Lynn held up her hand.

"Hold Up! Lisa! Hold Up!" She yelled. "Lisa! Stop! You will kill the man."

Lisa heard the words from faraway at first. But finally was able to get herself focused and under control. She was a bit embarrassed at the bloody pulp that lay at her feet. Her rage began to shift to sadness and she was bawling.

Gilbert's beating seemed to take forever, but really lasted less than three and a half minutes. William knew they were distracted so he went back into the factory. As Lisa let up on Gilbert and collected herself, she and Lynn began to look around. The decked out black pimp was heading for the car. But he had an extra piece of jewelry. A gun!

Lynn pushed her bike in front of the car in an effort to block their getaway but William shouted,

"Lynn! You get on out of here now! Benny, don't shoot her."

He had already jumped into the driver's seat and was revving the engine. Squealing tires threw gravel and dust into the air.

Then, everything got very quiet.

Lisa looked at Lynn.

"Lynn! What the fuck?"

It was one of those moments that was going to be the life changer. It would mark time. Both girls would reference things from before or after the factory. The girls discussed and re-discussed the details while keeping a watch on Gilbert. A full 30 minutes had passed.

Lynn looked at her friend. She knew this was going to have consequences for one or both.

"You better leave, Lisa," she said "I am going to call some people to try and find William before he gets too far out of town."

"But, I just beat the shit out of that man. I am not sure he is even breathing! Did he really rape you?"

"I hope that tennis racket can be washed."

Lisa looked at it. It was in remarkably good shape. No bends or imperfections. She thought she could just hose it off and it would be alright. There were fine little curls that were entwined inside the racket strings, though. Probably hair.

With tears sliding from her eyes, Lisa looked at Lynn.

"I would have killed him, if I had known, Lynn."

Lynn seemed to be thinking as she gestured for them to be out of Gilbert's ear shot. His bell had been rung pretty good, and he probably would never put two and two together. He was a junkie and maybe he would think this was just a drug deal gone bad.

They watched as Gilbert Morse slowly sat up from behind a grove of overgrown brush.

"….the hell? William, where are you at?"

He laid back down.

"Let's go," Lynn said. "I need to get back before Mama gets home. I am pretty sure that I won't be seeing William any time soon."

"Are you telling your mother about this situation? Are you going to do something about this fucker?"

"Not yet, my friend. I need some time to think."

They hugged goodbye.

Lynn

Throwing her bike down on the front lawn, Lynn marveled at how normal everything seemed to be. No matter what happens to you, the world will keep turning. It is something her grandmother often told her when she had a problem. She scrambled up the stairs to look at the clock. It was 4:45. She would have to get dinner started fast before her mother came home.

She went to the cupboard. There was Minute Rice in a box, a couple cans of tuna, red pinto beans in a bag, and an onion. Good grief! She couldn't even make red beans and rice. She ran down to the corner store. She grabbed two boxes of Chef BoyarDee complete spaghetti meals. Paul Hannon was the clerk. She knew that they marked up this food almost double there. Her mother said to use that store only as a last resort.

"Paul, please put this on Zenobia Parris' tab," she said.

"Ok Lynn, tell your mother her bill is at $25.00. No more charging until it's paid."

"Sure will," Lynn said with a grin showing all her teeth. "Thank you."

Once home, she opened the silver cylinders that contained spaghetti sauce. She quickly grabbed the peeling green saucepan, the only one this size, and poured in the sauce. She was just getting the spaghetti into the boiling water and punching holes into the little tin of parmesan cheese when her mother came through the door. It was after 6:00 PM but sometimes she worked late. Lynn tried to stay focused.

Hearing adult voices in the front room felt ominous. No one was laughing or upbeat. She looked through the kitchen door. It was her mother, her friend Lorraine, and a voice that Lynn didn't recognize. She popped her head in to say hello and there, looking right at her was Bobby Washington, Heaven's newest and now only black cop, and he had his hand on her mother's shoulder.

Her mother turned. Lynn saw her eyes were guarded. They were telling Lynn to stay quiet.

"Hello, Lynn," Mama said. "Have you heard the news?"

Lynn almost busted out laughing! Everything that happened today was news! A trafficking ring! Her stepfather abetting it with Gilbert Morse! The beating! She shook her head from side to side.

"What's happened, Mama?" she asked, not daring to show her emotion.

"Your stepfather's gone and got himself shot dead,." her mother said in a low voice. "And they think that it was Gilbert Morse who shot him."

Lynn's head reeled with all the possibilities of what might happen if Gilbert Morse was to tell his side of the story. She knew that it couldn't have been him because she left Gilbert laying on the ground and semi-conscious a little over an hour before.

"How do they know it was Gilbert?" She asked, and Bobby's head turned around to look at her full in the face.

"What's that supposed to mean, Lynn?" He asked, "Do you have something to tell us?"

Tread lightly, Lynn. She told herself. Don't give anything away.

"I'm just saying that William, you know, he had a lot of enemies. There's a lot of people I can think of that might want to hurt him before Gilbert Morse. He just doesn't seem to have it in him."

"Well, look who's sticking up for Gilbert," Mama's friend Lorraine piped in. "Thought you hated that old lech."

Lynn didn't say anything. She wasn't defending Gilbert, was she? This man had wronged her in the worst possible way. She decided to change the subject.

"Mama, have you eaten? I am just finishing making dinner."

"No, Lynn. You go ahead and feed the others. Bobby is taking me over to the county morgue in Paw Paw once they remove the body from the scene. I guess I need to identify the body. The good Lord knows he was not the best man, more like a thorn I got used to, but dead is dead after all."

"Do you want me to come along?" Lynn asked.

"I am going to be there for your mother, Lynn," Lorraine said. "I am her friend, start to finish."

"Okay, then," Lynn said, and she watched the trio head down the front porch steps. Bobby looked at her a long time after he got in the car. Or did he? She couldn't tell. She stood there and watched the car head east.

As quick as she could, she drained the spaghetti and threw a loaf of Wonder bread on the table. She put a stick of margarine on a small plate and figured this was going to have to do.

"Dinner is ready!" She yelled to her siblings. Her sisters came running in. "Yes! Chef BoyarDee! Thanks Lynn!"

Looking at her sisters, she said:

"I need you to help out here with cleaning up. I got to go look into something for Mama."

With that, she picked up the phone and dialed Lisa's number. Billy answered. She had a secret crush on him, but now was not the time to flirt.

"Hello, Billy. This is Lynn. Lamar's sister?"

"Hey," Billy said.

"Is Lisa available?" She heard the receiver crash down on the wall below in a bouncing way that indicated it was suspended by its circular cord. She heard a muffled exchange and then Lisa got on.

"Lynn! What's up?" Her voice was tentative. They didn't talk much on the phone, contact was made mainly at school.

"Lisa, William has been found dead. Shot. And they think it was Gilbert Morse."

Lisa sucked in the air, audibly, and then stopped breathing. She felt as if someone had pushed her backward down a hall that was getting narrower and narrower.

"But...I...Are they sure?"

"Now, listen." Lynn was talking fast. "We know it wasn't him. That means someone is out there killing people. The only people we saw at the factory this afternoon were you and me, Gilbert, William, the girl, and that man in the burgundy Cadillac."

"That's right. But I didn't see that man at all." Lisa said, "I do know the car was a Cadillac. Kind of like my dad's, only smooth on top. I think it was burgundy…"

"Listen, Lisa. We have to figure this out. For all we know that man will come back for us!"

"Well, that would be just dumb." Lisa said "If he's smart, he's far away."

"But then, if he was smart he wouldn't have killed one of his men first. Lisa, we are loose ends!"

Lisa's brother started to bother her for the phone. Billy didn't have any patience for his sisters.

"Quit hogging the phone!" He yelled, "I have an important call to make."

Lisa knew he was just going to go to the basement phone and mumble and pause with his girlfriend.

"Hey Lynn! I forgot I got your bike for you today. I will meet you at the corner of School and Lakeshore, in about ten minutes?"

Lynn knew Lisa didn't have her bike, she had taken it home. But she agreed to meet in ten minutes.

The spring-like weather ushered in a blanket of fog along the lakeshore. Lisa couldn't help thinking how much creepier this made things. She tried to stay in the shadows and not right under the streetlight.

Lynn came up the small hill breathing hard.

"We don't have much time. But I been thinking." She started,

"We have got to let Gilbert Morse fry in jail for this murder."

"I am so worried for that little girl," Lisa said. "We have to find the guy in the Cadillac."

"No, she wasn't from this area. I would know. I think she got away. But Bobby Washington took Mama over to Paw Paw to identify William's body. Maybe she will talk about it more. I just wanted to tell you not to say one word about this afternoon."

"I am afraid, Lynn. What if the guy comes back for us?"

"He wouldn't know you, Lisa. He was connected to the Zone. I bet he's never even seen Lake Shore Boulevard here."

"Is Gilbert in jail?" Lisa asked.

Lynn paused. "You know, no one ever said if they had picked him up, only that they thought he was the one who killed William. Oh shoot! What if Gilbert is stumbling around somewhere?"

Lisa wondered the same thing. There was something nagging in the back of her mind, though. The tennis racket! It was brand new. She saved a long time and ordered it through Tommy Shink, who ran the Sports section, inside the shoe store downtown. He always got deals for people who couldn't get into the larger cities for sports equipment. She loved the idea of being the only one in town with a Jimmy Conners 300. She wondered if the people even knew she was the one wailing on Gilbert. She couldn't shake off that angry bubble. It seemed to blur in one hot, raging moment. She felt like she could still be beating on him, if Lynn hadn't stopped her.

"Let's meet on the pool steps tomorrow before school," Lynn said. "Maybe I'll know more."

"Okay. Be safe."

Lynn turned around. Pumping her legs with all her might, she just made it inside the front door when she saw a car, rolling slow, go around the corner. It was so dark now, she couldn't tell the color. But it was a Cadillac. Lynn perspired as she tried to see it further down the street. All she could tell was its windows were black.

Lisa

Sadie gave Lisa a ride to school. Now that they had their driver's licenses, they wanted to go everywhere. Sadie got her own car, a little Pinto wagon. It was so cute. Lisa had to share a car with Billy which meant she might as well not have a car.

When they walked in the back of the school from the parking lot, there was Jed, waiting by the door.

Dammit, Lisa thought. I really don't want to get embroiled in anything with him.

"Good morning ladies!" he said brightly, "I brought you some doughnuts from the bakery."

"Yum! Thanks Jed," said Sadie. "I didn't eat when I left the house, and fifth hour lunch is killing me." She took a large bite of the doughnut. If Lisa didn't know better, she would think Sadie was flirting with Jed. Sadie *never* ate breakfast. Well, she hoped that Sadie could keep him away long enough. They hadn't spoken since Coach intervened. She was hoping it would just be understood that it was over.

Jed turned to Lisa and said,

"I got you a cinnamon roll. Nothing's too sweet for my girl."

Oh great, gag me, he's trying to be nice, Lisa thought.

"Sorry, Jed. I have a meeting this morning in the girl's locker room. And I am late."

She started to speed up and took the corner while sticking her right leg out for balance.

"That's it? That's all I get?" Jed had already started to rant. "I mean, what the fuck, Lisa?"

She let his shouting fade, concentrating on the task at hand. She pushed the whole idea of breaking up with him to the back of her mind. Now he was pissed. She would have to stay out in the open so he couldn't hurt her for snubbing him. But after what had happened with Gilbert, she knew she'd never let him hurt her again.

The steps were empty. The usual girls were not there. But neither was Lynn. Where was everyone? Oh, God! Oh, God! Could something have happened to Lynn?

"Lisa, psst," Lynn whispered from around the door post. "Let's walk in the pool auditorium. We still have our master keys from intramurals."

"Lynn, I couldn't sleep at all last night. I kept hearing cars go by and park at the end of the street by the lake. I was so afraid someone would come in that I went and slept at the foot of my sister's bed."

"We have every right to be scared," Lynn said and she began to tell the story of how her evening ended.

Her mother and Lorraine got into the house around 10:30 PM. Her mama was so tired that Lorraine just muttered a few things to her and made for home. When she came into the kitchen, Lynn gave her a plate of hot food, which she picked at. While they were sitting together quietly in the kitchen, the phone rang. Mama told Lynn to answer but there was just breathing on the other end.

Lynn hung up, the fear written all over her face. Her mother told her she had no reason to be nervous. It seemed that her stepfather and Gilbert Morse had gotten into a terrible fight. Gilbert had been beaten up by something awful. They were both found lying in the ravine down by Deerlick Park.

"What was that, Mama?" Lynn asked, "Did you say they found Gilbert *with* William?"

"Yes, they did. William was no longer breathing, but Gilbert still had a faint heartbeat. He had been shot as well. There were drugs strewn around the bodies and Bobby Washington figured that the crime scene people would determine that it was a drug deal gone bad."

"Mama?" Lynn started to list questions and her mother held up her hand.

"I am just too tired for more questions, Lynn. Please let me go to bed."

"So, that's all I know," Lynn said as she finished relaying the information to Lisa.

"Wait!" Lisa said, stopping the story. "That's good, right? If everyone believes that it was mutual, no one will ever know we saw anything."

"Yeah. It could have been good for us, Lisa. But, unfortunately, they found a third body after my mama got to the county morgue."

"I hope you are going to tell me it is the guy in the Cadillac." Lisa groaned.

"No. Lisa. It was a girl about the age of 12. She had beaded cornrows in her hair like the girl we saw."

"Well, now we are going to have to talk to the police!" Lisa shouted and she started to walk faster. Her face was shiny from the humidity of the pool area and her voice echoed so loudly that Lynn put her hand over Lisa's mouth.

"Okay. I'll whisper. Tell me about the girl. Why would anyone *kill* a girl?" Lisa said. Her face was beginning to contort into tears. "I mean, did she know too much? Was she able to tell who these people are? I mean, we can tell all the players except the Burgundy Cadillac guy. Oh God! That's it, isn't it, Lynn, she knew who he was or she could ID him? Oh we are so dead!" She said wailing.

Lynn slapped her.

"This is not the time to go soft." She said, "Gilbert Morse is not dead. Not even close. Mama said that William was shot right between the eyes. One shot was all they could find. He wasn't beat up like Gilbert. They think Gilbert got shot in the chest a couple times, but he is expected to recover."

"Oh holy shit," Lisa mouthed. "He might remember us."

"Right." Lynn said, "Won't the police be so interested in how and what we saw? Won't they wonder why we hadn't bothered to share information? But that's not the worst part."

"Great," Lisa said, feeling herself becoming dizzy from the chlorine filled pool room..

"That gun was never recovered! They don't think that Gilbert actually shot William. So, now, Mama said a crime team from Lansing is coming here to do a thorough investigation."

"Mother F," Lisa said, then as it hit her, "Where did they find the girl?"

"It was up the river someplace. Fronter or Ford's? It's an old fishing lodge. It's been deserted for some time."

"I don't even know where that is," Lisa said, "Do you think the burgundy Cadillac guy is gone?"

"I think he got too good of a look at us," Lynn said. "We are not going to be comfortable until he's caught."

The bell for the first hour rang. The girls agreed to meet after the tennis match. It was a home match and should be over fast. Heaven had a few girls that knew how to play, but the really good tennis players left for larger cities in the fall. The sport had just been added for girls a year ago since Title 9. They were playing one of the towns over by Kalamazoo. It was likely the team of girls that were playing at places like Kalamazoo College and various racket clubs in their area. Lisa anticipated a quick loss.

At lunch, she could not avoid Jed any longer.

"What the hell is up with you?" He asked angrily, "Either you are my girlfriend, with time only for ME or we are through. What is it going to be?"

"Jed, this is not a good place to talk," Lisa began.

"Not a good place to talk? Why? Because I might do this?" He took his tray of mashed potatoes and turkey gravy and turned it over on her head. "I don't have to wait for your decision. I don't want you anymore. I tried, just remember that. I tried."

Two teachers who saw the whole thing happen, were on him like white on rice. They didn't like this macho piece of shit. He was all the talk in the teacher's lounge, and now there was a chance to suspend him.

"Get your fucking hands off me, you idiots." He snarled, "I know how this goes down. No one is going to blame the poor damsel in distress over there are they? You are all such a bunch of amateurs."

A group of students rushed over to Lisa, who was covered in the congealed remnants of Jed's lunch. One of them went to the office and came back with a pass for Lisa to go home. She got up, and with most of the food wiped off her face, went to the locker room.

Ms. Aitch was on her lunch break and the place was empty. She sat back, deep in her office, listening to blues music and smoking a Virginia Slims Menthol cigarette. Her one piece gym suit showed off how very thin she was. Her ashy brown skin and rolled down anklets made her look more like 16 than 26.

"Don't rat me out." She chuckled. "I am just trying to balance the fresh smoke with the stale smoke from the stalls. Why these girls come in here to smoke is beyond me…" She was going to keep going on, rambling when Lisa came around the corner. She took in her stained clothes and hair stuck together with the tan goo.

"Ms. Aitch, I am sure this was an accident, I'm sure he didn't mean to do it."

Lisa began her argument on the offensive.

Ms. Aitch did a once over. She saw the shambles of a new sweater, the long hair matted in congealed grease and gravy, food still caked along her jawbone, an obvious attempt to wipe as much off the face as possible.

"Oh Hell No, Lisa!" She cried, "If that poor excuse for a boyfriend did this, then we are going to have a serious problem."

"Ms. Aitch, I am trying to break up with him. This is minor. In fact, I feel like celebrating, because not only did he break up with me in there, but he got suspended from school!"

"Listen to me. I am going to say this one time. Never lay down for a man. You hear me? You have got the whole world at your feet, and you settle for some nasty, half-bred, loser with no class or no chance of learning it? Uh uh! Girl, get in that shower. You can use my shampoo but you have got a tennis match today and Goodman's bus will be here in 30 minutes!"

Lisa let herself be pushed along. It was a bit embarrassing. She should be humiliated about what just went occured in front of her whole lunch group. Everyone must be shocked and laughing about it now. But she didn't care. She was rid of Jed Adams for good. She felt almost giddy when she stepped into the shower.

Lynn

Walking into her house after school, Lynn was uneasy. Everyone had activities to do and she was hoping to have some company to pass the time until Mama came home. She had been looking over her shoulder all day. She considered going out to her grandparents to stay for a while. But dammit, there was the victim. Her heart ached for the young girl and she wondered how that crime scene was being assessed. She decided to go out there on her bike.

The new River Bike Trail was recently completed and it took Lynn less than ten minutes to get closer to the river where old fishing warehouses still stood. She saw rusted relics of poles and bobbers, portions of nets with floats of silver, buckets, and used up old junk.

It wasn't hard to spot the place she was looking for. It had a peeling sign that still spelled out "orte" with an 'f' missing but still faintly recognizable. The bright yellow crime tape cordoned off the area neatly so that quadrants could be studied and scrutinized. There was a small crowd of curiosity seekers prowling around with their instamatic cameras. One man had a Polaroid Instant Camera and was discarding the negatives he peeled off behind a tree, away from the police area. Lynn waited for him to leave, then picked up the negatives. She stuffed them in her bike bag to look at later and followed the crowd around the old building.

Periodically, a policeman would come out and yell at the gawkers to go home. He acted like this kind of thing happened in Heaven every day. Yawning, he got out a toothpick and asked one of the camera people if they knew the score of the Tigers game. He was obviously from Lansing, Lynn deduced, no one followed the Tigers this close to Chicago. White Sox or Cubs all the way.

She decided that nothing was going to be gained here, so she walked to her bike and picked it up. There was a note sticking out from under her seat. She quickly put it in her bike bag and took off pedaling until she got to the beach. She opened it up and there was a hastily written note. It said:

"Got information. South Beach 10:30 PM."

She took off like a shot. What if someone was watching?

Obviously, someone knew of her involvement in this mystery.

She got to the tennis courts just as the sun was disappearing into Lake Michigan in peaches, pinks, and golds. It was close to 6:30 PM. Lisa was walking off her court with the smile of victory on her face. Her dad was in the car watching and gave a little honk and thumbs up when he left. Lisa was driving home as she usually did on game days.

Lynn waited for the people to thin out and then went up to Lisa and showed her the note.

The smile drained off Lisa's face like butter off a hot cob of corn. Who was out at the crime scene that could have written the note?

Lynn searched her brain and said there were so many people taking pictures and milling around, that she hadn't seen each person. The cars had to park a long distance away and she hadn't even thought to look for a car there.

"I think we should tell Bobby Washington." Lisa said, "You know, you can tell him what Gilbert Morse did to you and he won't tell anyone."

"Bobby is a good friend of my mother, Lisa." Lynn said, "I do not want her to know this. She says she didn't love my stepfather, but this information would make her feel as if it was her fault, somehow."

"Lynn, why would Bobby tell her? He loves her."

"You may be right, Lisa. But first let's just see who has information."

"So, you are saying we go alone? Just be sitting ducks for a killer?" Lisa was getting wound up.

"Look." Lynn whispered, "the person only left information for me. What if you wait on the dune, and if something happens, use this."

She pushed a small brown paper bag into Lisa's hands. Inside, wrapped in a baggie, was a handgun. It was heavy and surprisingly small. Lisa's eyes went wide as saucers.

"Are you crazy? We can't have a gun! Where'd you get this thing?"

"Relax." Lynn said, "I was checking out the route down Lakeshore to Deerlick. I found this on 16th Street. Someone must have tossed it. It makes sense that this could be the gun they are looking for."

"And you picked it up? And you are giving it to me? No way, Lynn. No way." Lisa backed up as if the gun was radioactive. "If we don't turn that gun in, we could be in really big trouble."

"We will turn it in, Lisa. But we have to make sure it has Gilbert's fingerprints on it." Lynn continued,

"I think it's loaded. If I recall there's a safety to remove." She fiddled around through the baggie with the gun. "See, here." She pointed to the safety button. "Make sure that is off if you have to use it."

"Oh sweet Jesus!" Lisa lamented, "How did things get this far out of hand?"

"We need to focus," Lynn said. "We might not even need to use that. Let's meet up at the top of the dune at about 10:00 PM. You can probably sneak out, right?"

"No one ever checks on me after I turn in, but I do have to think about not waking Jane. She will wake Mom and Dad for sure."

"Tell her ahead of time that you are meeting with me," Lynn said. "She likes me. Explain about my momma being sad and you are just, I don't know, going to sit with her?"

"Lynn, I haven't been inside your house in my whole life! She will never believe that!"

Lynn was getting annoyed and it showed in her face. Her eyes were squinting and the muscles in her jaw were flexing and relaxing.

"Okay. I will get out somehow," Lisa said. "But I say we give Bobby a heads up about this."

"We don't have time," Lynn said "My mother is going to wonder where I have been. I have to go make dinner and there are surely people around the house that will need me."

"Okay." Lisa mumbled, "But this gun is not going to be used."

"Fine, just put it in your gym bag. I threw the bag away that I had it in. Try not to put any fingerprints on it either," Lynn added "I got to go" They parted with a plan albeit wobbly.

Lisa

Lisa decided that she would not even take the gun from the gym bag. She'd keep the whole thing in the car. What was Lynn even thinking?

She began to pull into the driveway but the twins were playing basketball using the hoop on the garage. They indicated to park on the street.

"Heard you won your match," Tim said. "Good for you."

"Thanks," Lisa said as she dragged her books and tennis gear out of the car.

"Hey! Don't forget your gym bag," Tommy said. "Your clothes will stink up the car for Billy's date tonight."

"He can't go on a date during a school night!" She shouted.

"He can when it's Stag Night at the yacht club and Mom has Bridge at Richman's."

How could she have forgotten? Tuesday night? Her parents wouldn't be home until after 11:30 PM. Jane would need to be tucked in. With Billy gone, she would have to babysit! This plan was not going to work!

She got into the house just as her dad was walking out!

"You did good. You might want to move your feet more than

just stand there waiting," he critiqued. "But overall, you were alright." With that, he went out to the front driveway and got into his Cadillac. As he sped away, Lisa looked at the boys in the other drive still playing ball.

"Mom?" She called, "Is Billy babysitting tonight? I have a project to work on later."

"Why, of course he is," her mother said without blinking an eye. "Make sure you aren't too late."

"So, can I use the car since it's almost after dark?" She asked, ready to blow back out before her brother got wind of her taking the car.

"I suppose. Just, make sure you are home early. It's a school night."

"Yeah. I'll work for an hour or two. I will be back as soon as I can."

"You make it sound like you are doing some secret operation." Her mother chuckled. She smelled like she had taken a bath in Estee Lauder perfume. Her lipstick was red and she was packing cigarettes into a case. Bridge nights with these eight smoking ladies was like having a campfire in the living room. She pitied the Richman kids. They'd go to school with smoke hangovers.

'Billy!" Mom yelled down the basement stairs. "I am leaving and you are in charge."

Lisa started running toward the car. She was going to have to hang out somewhere for two and a half hours and keep the car unseen in town. She decided she'd go visit her great grandmother in Glenn. No, that wouldn't work, her great grandma went to bed at sun set. She peeked over her shoulder and there stood Billy, his arms crossed and he was shaking his head.

She started up the car. Looking behind her into the back seat, she realized that her gym bag was inside the garage entrance. She left it there to pick up later, to put inside the car before she left. With her brother standing there all pissed off, there was no way she could get out of the car and retrieve the bag. But she knew she had to before the little boys looked inside. She drove to the turnaround area. There was Lake Michigan. She was angry tonight. White capped waves were being blown to shore by a west wind. She saw Sadie taking down the flag from the pole.

"Hey Sadie!" She yelled above the roar of the waves. Sadie waved and came over to the car.

"I see you survived your baptism by gravy," she cracked.

Lisa was not in the mood to joke around.

"Look. I promise I will explain this all to you but I need your help. Billy is mad that I have the car. He and Lyndsey were supposed to go out tonight, but I copped the car before he got it."

"And…?" Sadie interjected.

"I need my gym bag. It's right inside the garage where the boys are just finishing up their game. Billy's going to try and stop me. I need that bag before my mom leaves for bridge. Will you go up there and grab it and put it in the car as I go by?"

"I don't want Billy mad at me!" She yelled, "He almost pulled my hair out when I was telling Lyndsey something he didn't want her to know. How'm I supposed know they have so many secrets? Are you sure I can't get you something of mine to use?"

"I just need my gym bag and I don't want him coming after

me." Lisa said, noticing that the coast was clear, "Forget it. I am just going to run up there and get it while he's inside." She put the car in drive.

As she pulled into the second drive she ran out leaving the door open. Odd, she thought, he's not coming out. She threw the bag in the car and gunned it to the stop sign. Looking to her left, she saw Billy, on his bike, smiling and waiting. He rode the bike right out in front of the car.

"You are not going anywhere with my car." He said in a dangerous voice. "You'd better have your ass back in an hour or I am going to come and find you and personally give you up to dad. Now, git out."

Lisa never realized how much she purely hated her brother. She knew people who had brothers who were loving and supportive. Not hers. The old macho double standard was alive and well and living in her house.

"Fine, Billy. Fine." she said, as she slid out of the car with her engine still running. "Let me at least take your bike."

He laughed then. She looked closely, he hadn't taken his bike but hers. She was really getting angry. He said, "If you aren't careful, Mom and Dad are going to have to hear about your scene in the cafeteria today. It's all over school."

"Oh, will you tell them, Billy? You have a few million skeletons in your closet. I wonder if I should start letting Mom and Dad know just what you are up to yourself. You are such a little boy. Fighting over your toy. Take the damn car. Leave me the hell alone. And you better not leave the twins and Jane by themselves."

Lisa was mad. She took her duffel bag and put it on the handlebars of the bike. What a shitty person! What had she ever done to him? He put her down at every turn, laughed at all her accomplishments as if they were amusing, even got the rest of the family laughing at her over her writing that was published in the paper.

She headed north down Lakeshore Boulevard without a backward glance.

Lynn

Lynn started walking down the side streets to the beach. Black girls were rarely seen on Lakeshore Boulevard and she didn't want to drive suspicion. When she got to the Catholic Church she crossed the street and slid slowly down the dune. Beach grass was slashing her legs, and the last glimmers of sunset paled as twilight turned into night. Stars were out and the scene was breathtaking but Lynn reminded herself to keep her head in the game. The church bell chimed ten times. Things were about to get real in about 30 minutes.

To her right there was a rustling sound. Her mouth got dry. Backing into the shadow she caught sight of Lisa hiding her bike and gym bag underneath a small bush.

"Lisa!" She whispered.

"It's me, I'm here," Lisa said.

"Why did you ride your bike?"

"Long story. Are you ready for this?"

"Yes. I am going to walk around the hill and come down by the road. Do you think it's light enough to see?"

"I can see. But Lynn, what if you need to get out of there fast?"

"I will scream and run. You go right to the police and ask for Bobby Washington. I think I agree about bringing him into this for our safety. If I don't see you, I will talk to you later tonight."

"I think I am going to barf," Lisa said.

Lynn smiled at her and Lisa could see her beautiful teeth as they reflected the street light.

"This is exciting, Lisa! We may bring down these mother-fuckers on our own!"

"Is there any word about Gilbert?" Lisa asked.

"No, he hasn't come to yet, and if he has, his jaw is wired shut. It got broke…"

"Did I do that, Lynn? Did I break his jaw?"

"Does it matter right now, Lisa?" Lynn said. She began disentangling herself from the vines and undergrowth on the hill.

"Well, I've got your back. Let's do this," Lisa said bravely.

"That's what I want to hear," Lynn said smiling, and off she went up the sand hill and onto the sidewalk.

Lisa's stomach began to growl. She reviewed her day. Well, she should have eaten that cinnamon roll that Jed brought, she thought wryly. What a long ass day. She began watching for Lynn to reemerge around the corner. She looked at her watch; 10:28 PM. Where was she?

Scanning the shoreline and seeing nothing, she began to get agitated. Was that a silhouetted figure moving slowly up from the south or were her eyes playing tricks on her? Lynn appeared into view and marched around the kiddy swing set under the halo of the parking lot light. The power plant was chugging away bringing in lake water to be used by every resident in the city.

But damn, this place was loud. Voices could never be heard above the din.

A car came around the old trolley stop on the river side, north of the power plant and parked alongside the darkened building. It proved a major distraction as its lights were off. Lisa felt a tug in her gut. Was this their courier? Seconds passed. No one got out of the car. Lynn looked briefly in her direction. Stay put, Lisa thought to herself. Let them come to you.

A tall figure came off the beach then. A man. He was thinner than the guy from the Cadillac. Who the hell was this?

Lynn turned around. She seemed very at ease with this person. She was deeply involved in conversation and in just seconds her body language changed. She began gesturing with her hands, he kept pointing his finger in her face. Something about that finger pointing was so familiar.

Oh. My. God. The man was Jed! He was beginning to wind up like the times he went over the top and began punching. She had to get Lynn out of there before he hurt her. She left everything under the bush and flew down the dune, feet sinking knee deep into the newly dredged sand. She knew she wasn't going to get there in time. Breathing in enough air to yell out, she stopped. The car that was parked by the power plant turned on its lights. Jed stood frozen for a full five seconds. He was trying to figure out what to do. He pushed Lynn to the ground and spat the only discernible words, "You'll be sorry, bitch."

The car was a light blue Camaro. It came barreling out of its hiding place full force. Clearly, the driver was after Jed. He bypassed Lynn and went as far on the concrete as he could.

Lynn stayed down. The driver finally gave up the chase with the car. There was no way to follow someone on the beach except on foot. I guess that means me, Lisa thought, knowing she had a visual on Jed as he ran. Coming in at an angle, she closed the distance between them. He picked his way easily through the series of paths leading up the dune to the road. Jed knew this area well, but so did she. He was making for the Blue Stairs that led up to Lakeshore Boulevard. There were just feet between them and he was almost to the top. She opened her mouth to say something when a car pulled up. A Cadillac. A burgundy Cadillac. He got in the passenger side as it sped away.

Her mind was reeling. It all was making sense now. Jed Adams, his temper, the lack of empathy. He was wrapped up in this trafficking ring. Shit! Shit! Shit!

Defeated, she turned and went down to the packed, damp sand near the water. Taking off her shoes, she ran back to the beach parking lot but slowed as she neared the swings. Lynn was standing up. A tall, muscular man was standing with her and he had a notepad out and was scribbling fast notes. Looking straight into the power plant spotlights she couldn't see who it was. Lynn began calling to her:

"Lisa. It's okay. Come down here. I'm all right."

Lisa couldn't take her eyes off the man. As he got more into focus, she recognized his short afro and mustache. It was Bobby Washington!

"Lisa, I told Bobby to come," Lynn continued.

Bobby began explaining:

"I have been working deep cover on child trafficking cases

for months. What we ran across is a corridor that brings teens and children to a central point right here in Heaven. They get approved by the overseer and they get shipped to other countries. From here they usually go to Detroit then to Canada. Some make it back to the U.S., but by that time, they are used up addicts. There isn't a big market for them."

"Looks like we got tangled up in something much bigger than we thought," Lynn said.

"But that young girl couldn't have been more than 11 or 12. Why didn't they just ship her off? They killed her?"

"Well, she was a good listener when Lynn told her to follow the tracks, she did. But, Bennie Forter, Jed's dad, had Jed take her out as soon as she got to the river, we think. She was moved to the shack and was only stumbled upon by a few over-curious boys looking for new fishing lures."

Bobby continued, "Your boy Jed Adams is one of the leaders of the group. They figured that if he could work in this area and still stay in high school, he could work both angles. Get the cargo in and out."

Lisa looked confused. Bobby felt sorry for her. Young love was often misguided but this poor girl was totally used for her name and her status in the town. No one would mess with her father and so Jed thought it was a great cover for him to be her boyfriend.

"So, let me get this straight." Lisa began, "Jed Adams is who you think murdered that girl. Just because she might know something like a face or a name?"

"That's unfortunately correct. Did you know what his name

was before he was adopted?" Bobby asked calmly, helping her through each detail.

"Um. I know he told Sadie and me once when we first met him, something like Farther or Foster." Lisa said, catching her breath.

"Do you think it could be Forter?" Bobby asked.

"That's it! Forter. But of course he lied and said his father was long gone."

Bobby chuckled then, "Until he came back and showed his little boy the tricks of his trade. He started out as a pimp but found there was better money to be made in moving young girls and little boys. He'd sell them to buyers who would use them up as children and, if they survived, he'd pimp them out as adults. Seems as if your friend Jed was what they call an Influencer. He would find vulnerable children and cultivate them until he could control them. Having you for a 'girlfriend' made him look like a regular high school student. But he is so very dangerous. I'm sure you have some stories for me."

This made Lisa very uncomfortable. This was sickening. How many times, early on, had Jed told her to trust him? How many beatings did he give her that he had already given to other girls? Why was it so hard to break up with him? But here she was, after 11:00 PM on the beach with a cop telling her that she truly was living a lie.

"Look, I've got to get home. I am toast if my parents know I am even here," she said empathically. "Bobby, can you put my bag and bike in your car and give me a ride to my street?"

"Well, of course. I won't have you or Lynn out at night for a while. With your information, Lynn, we will be able to link Jed to Edwin Forter and to two of the murders. There are several cold cases that the FBI is studying at the moment."

"Hold on," Lisa said. "The man in the burgundy Cadillac is a black man. I mean, have you looked at Jed Adams? He has blue eyes and very pale skin."

"Just like his mother. That fact of him "passing" was one of the things about this case that was the missing link. But out at the old fishing shack today, I met a man who claimed his grandson was a Forter. He said he went by Jed Adams but Adams was the stepdad's name. So, I visited the Adams' house and Mrs. Adams showed me some pictures of Jed as a child. His father was a black man. She confirmed that also. She was embarrassed to tell me. Said I would never be able to tell anyone,"

"But they are still on the loose," Lisa said. "How are we supposed to live now?"

"Look, it's only Tuesday. You two will go to school tomorrow as if nothing happened," Bobby said.

"I mean, what about his argument with Lynn?" Lisa asked.

It was Lynn's turn to pipe in, "He was mad about you breaking up with him. He wanted to talk to me about you! The information was a big fake to get me to get you to get back together with him."

"Well, that isn't happening." Lisa said.

"I wonder if maybe it could for a while," Bobby interjected. "Jed didn't see you here tonight, right? So, he figured you had your tennis match and then went home. If you pretended to go back with him, maybe to eke out a little information? I mean,

I am working with the FBI. We'd protect you."

"But my brother knows what happened in the lunchroom today and so does everyone at school. I can't take the humiliation," Lisa whispered.

"Listen," Bobby said. "Just see him away from school. Tell him your parents are really pissed and you really want to get together but can't look like it yet."

"My dad really hates him," Lisa said, "and Jed's suspended for a week."

"Work with Lynn and me," Bobby said. Then looking at Lynn he said, "I hope I am not putting words in your mouth. Your stepfather was a terrible man and that Gilbert Morse is so fried on drugs, they probably will never get a straight story from him."

"Of course I am IN," Lynn said. "But you and I need to talk further about Gilbert Morse."

They dropped Lisa off and she jumped on her bike and glided down the hill to her house. To her good luck, her parents weren't home yet and the 'teen car' she shared with her brother was in the driveway. Sneaking into the garage by the back door she went immediately into her bedroom. She carefully hid her gym bag way in the back of her closet with her shoes, and putting on her pajamas, made a run for the kitchen grabbing a banana and a glass of milk. Standing there thinking about all that had happened in a few short hours she watched a car do a slow roll up the street. No one needed to tell her that it was the burgundy Cadillac.

Her heart started beating so fast she could hear it in her ears. Her face was on fire and she felt dizzy. With fingers like clay, she misdialed and redialed Sadie's number. Sadie had her own line.

"Hullo," Sadie said, as if she had been fast asleep.

"Sadie. Was Jed at your house tonight?" Lisa asked. "I mean I am not mad or anything."

"Look. What's happening with you two?" Sadie asked. " He came over her for an hour and a half crying about getting you back."

"Did he tell you what happened in the cafeteria today?" Lisa asked. "He is kicked out for a week."

"Yes, he didn't have to tell me. I saw it. Quite frankly, I think you are better to be rid of him." Sadie said, "His temper is ugly. I told him I had to go to sleep and he wouldn't leave. He kept checking the street."

"Well, when did he leave, because I just saw the burgundy Cadillac go up the street a couple minutes ago?"

"Burgundy Cadillac? Ha-ha. He was driving his Chevelle," Sadie said.

"Are you sure?" Lisa asked with sweat beginning to run down the back of her neck.

"Yes. Because my dad came home from the yacht club and he came in and said someone needs to move the Chevelle. Hey. Are you okay?"

"Yeah. Thanks Sadie. I've got to go. I am really sorry I woke you."

Tossing and turning in her bed, Lisa couldn't help but feel that this nightmare simply wasn't going to end. Was the driver driving that burgundy Cadillac after her? To kill? Why did Jed go to Sadie's? How did he get his Chevelle? She felt embarrassed that the boy she'd been dating was using her in this way.

The clock clicked to one and she could hear all the dad's on the block pulling into their driveways, one by one. Her mother was dropped off within minutes of her dad. They made their way to the stairs, quietly sharing the gossip of the day. Her dad's voice stopped outside her door.

"Oh shit," she said under her breath.

Very quietly the door opened. Her dad made it over to her top bunk. She could smell the bourbon on his breath. He shook her. She rolled toward him.

"Dad?"

"If that scrawny bastard ever touches you or lays a hand on you, I will kill him. Let that sink in. No daughter of mine will be humiliated by some lowlife trash."

"It's okay, dad. It's over," Lisa said.

"You're goddam right it's over," he yelled. "Son of a Bitch! The whole bridge club told your mother. Can you even imagine how she felt? I wonder how many people knew at the yacht club. Because if those biddies at cards knew.... Son of a bitch." He made for the door.

"You are grounded. The only things you can do are: go to school and tennis. That's it. You hear me?"

"W-w-wait a minute." Lisa sat up in bed, "I'm grounded? But Dad, I didn't do anything."

"No, you did not. Not one damn thing. You didn't tell us it had happened! Hell, you played a tennis match today. You didn't come to us at ALL."

"Um. No I did not. Because, quite frankly, I knew this is

what would happen."

"Well, you better get used to coming straight home and I'll tell you, if I ever see that little asshole, I will punch him right in the nose. Don't think I won't."

Jane was sniffling on the bottom bunk when he closed the door.

"It's okay, Jane." Lisa whispered, "He's mad at me not at you."

Lynn

Buzz! Buzz!

Lynn's alarm was going off! She reached out her hand to turn it off only to find that her hand was not able to reach the nightstand. It was stopped by something. Chains?

Coming fully awake now, it hit her that the sounds she was hearing was not her alarm. She looked up and saw a gigantic Cicada on the ripped screen. It was stuck to the screen and she watched it in terror. She hated bugs! But it was doing something weird. It seemed to leave its old skin on the screen and climb out with a totally intact one. That was bomb! Funny how little things like that can distract you from what terror lies before you.

She tried to remember how she got here. It was Jed Adams. He stopped her as she was walking home from school Monday. Said something had happened to Lisa and he needed her help. Of course she jumped right into his car. But then he was driving north ending up at this nasty little shack. As she was begging him to let her go he put chains on her hands and clicked the lock around an exposed board in the wall. He promised he wasn't going to hurt her, he just needed her out of the way.

An entire day passed. She wasn't hurt by Jed, in fact, she

talked to him a lot about his love of hunting, his feeling of never belonging, his desire to be a good person, and even his demons. But, try as she might to convince him that he needed to let her go, he simply would not budge. It was nothing personal he told her. She just fit a profile. They talked late into the night.

Lynn channeled her grandmother's common sense. I am chained to a bed. Jed Adams is my captor. I am out somewhere north of Heaven down an old road. I am on a mattress that smells like Aunt Mable's attic. I have to pee really bad.

"Jed?" She called, "Jed, I really have to use the restroom."

He must not have been far away. He came on to the porch from inside the cabin and sneered.

"I can see you pee. Do it right here," He said.

She tried to laugh. "Jed, have you ever seen a woman on her period? It is not an exciting thing to watch. Now, I need to clean up. Please, be the man that Lisa says you are and let me use the restroom."

At the mention of Lisa's name, Jed straightened up.

"Does she really think I am a good person?" He asked.

"She thinks you are made for her." Lynn lied. "She wouldn't go through all the stuff she has, if she didn't love you."

Jed seemed to accept what she said, because he began unlocking her chains.

"Sorry to say, no proper restroom for milady," he said. "Walk behind that little bush over there. Keep one hand where I can see it."

He watched her walk to the bush. He hunted deer on and off season out here since he was small. His father and he often used it as a base where they could meet and make plans. If she tried to run, there was a deep ravine that cut it off from all other land to the south and if she ran north, she ran right back into the cliff that surrounded the place. He smiled. They all thought he was some hick kid.

He observed her for a bit and realized that she really wasn't going anywhere; why not give her some privacy? He went back in and took out his magazines. The centerfolds were well worn. If only his girlfriend would put out for him.

Lynn couldn't believe her luck when she saw Jed go back inside. She scanned her surroundings. There sure weren't many choices. Taking her jacket off, she hung it on a branch in such a way that it looked as though she was still there. She backed away from the bush and picked her way through pricker bushes and thorny vines. Preparing to run, Lynn noticed the ground was falling away. She looked ahead and saw a deep ravine. Water was draining from it into the lake. She followed it until she heard the rushing of the waves. She could get away if she got on the solid sand of the beach. Gravity was pulling her down the side of the ravine, ever so slowly, as she held the small trees and bushes along the way. Damp leaf litter held onto her bare arms and its slimy wetness made her shudder. With only a few yards left, she saw Jed. He was on the beach and watching her.

He bent over laughing when he saw the look on her face.

"You stupid black bitch.." he yelled. "Did you really think you could get away from here?"

Shifting, she began to climb the other way. She wasn't sure how he had made it to the beach so quickly, but if she could just get back to the gravel road, and out to the highway and to safety. Her hand gripped a tiny oak sapling that managed to take root on the top side of the ravine. Hefting herself, full weight, she realized it was not going to hold her. Toppling end over end, she actually bounced in the air before hitting her head on a large rock embedded halfway inside the creek bed. The lights in her head flickered then went out.

Jed found her laying at the bottom of the ravine.

"Goddammit." He swore.

As he assessed Lynn, he realized he had been in this position before, a couple years back. He was bow hunting off season and wounded a deer. He found her in the ravine and dragged her along the beach to the old mining trolley track. Although this trolley hadn't worked in at least 50 years, a car still could make it up and down the high bluff propelled by a pull chain he had rigged. Racing back to the shack, Jed looked for the old moth eaten carpet he had used. Picking through the odds and ends of lanterns and camping gear, he found it in the corner. He chucked things left and right. He couldn't take the chance on Lynn waking up. He put the rolled up carpet on the trolley track and watched it slide down as if a child at the park. He gathered it up at the bottom and reaching Lynn, saw that she hadn't moved.

"Shit!" He said aloud. She'd better be alive. He slapped her face gently. It was hard not to give it a full swing. He marveled at how a little thing like slapping a girl or beating her a little gave him a primal satisfaction. He had half a mind to start in on Lynn, but she was moaning.

With Lynn not fully conscious, it was easy to wrap her up

in the carpet. He suspected she would tap out again once he got her rolled up. She had blood leaking out of her ears. Her nose bled also. That rock really rang her bell, Jed thought. I am going to have to treat her with kid gloves before I turn her over.

He knew the traffickers well. Lately, they asked for girls to be delivered to them. In earlier days, they picked up random female hitchhikers or stoned panhandlers on the streets. They wanted girls with no family looking for them. He wondered how Lynn's family would react. He didn't want Lamar to know he was involved with her; he had friends in the Black Disciples Gang out of Chicago.

Jed's father had a long and dark feud with that gang. He stole a lot of their business when he was in the drug trade. Jed knew his father felt as if trafficking live women was almost on the up and up. He saw many well-known businessmen bid on the girls in various locations, like the inside of barns or deserted resorts all up and down the coasts of the Great Lakes. The trade went back at least 100 years when the fairs and traveling carnivals would provide rental of women to the stoic old farmers and conservative tradesmen along their circuits. Ironically, these traffickers came by way of Amsterdam and many girls were sent as "Cargo" over to Europe for a stretch.

He heard a car up on the drive. That would be TJ. It was perfect timing.

Lisa

Lisa really wasn't so worried about being grounded. It made the "mission" just a little more exciting. Her dad had really been hot. It was very unlikely that she could sneak out at night now. With Jed out of school, she had some decisions to make. It went against her grain to lie to anyone, but she knew that the stakes of preventing another death were sitting squarely on her and Lynn's shoulders.

She let a few days pass to absorb the quagmire of events. People were dying. Somehow, she was mixed up in this crazy shit and she felt she may never leave her house again. But she wanted justice for the little girl more than anything else. She wanted justice for herself too.

As she got ready for school, she planned her day. She hadn't talked to Lynn in a few days and they hadn't crossed paths at school. She had to find out where Jed was. She had to find him somehow and maybe talk him into having a powwow with her. She knew he loved her. It wasn't something she made up. She knew she had a certain power over him. She could feign sickness and skip practice tomorrow. The team was terrible and she knew no amount of practice could salvage this year.

Her plan to locate Jed shaped up as she drew it out in her journal last night. The problem was getting him a message. She decided to ask his stepbrothers.

Artie insisted on driving her to school. There really wasn't anything as humiliating. He pulled up to the drop-off area in front of the high school and she grumpily opened the door. The bitches in the front office watched her walk by the opened door with each secretary giving her a knowing nod. Oh, they had been filled in by her dad, for sure. He watched her walk into the doors and waited a couple seconds to make sure she didn't walk back out. Artie Palma on high alert was something she didn't need right now. She scanned the sitters on the ledge. No sign of the stepbrothers. Then she spotted the swimmers getting out of practice, their hair wet and eyes bloodshot from chlorine. She waited.

"Hey TJ.?" A voice yelled from behind the door, "Tastee Shack at three thirty? Jill is working and we can scam some free burgers!"

"Can't," TJ. Adams said, as he emerged from the pool doors. "Jed is letting me use his car and I have to get it back to him after school. He and my mom got into it last night and he stayed out at the cabin."

"Man. You really got stuck with him when your dad married his mom." His teammate said. "I'd rather have V.D. At least I know it will go away eventually."

"Yeah. He's a real case." TJ. said, "I think my dad is re-evaluating this whole marriage thing. He and my stepmom are always arguing about Jed. My stepmom was actually defending that move he made in the cafeteria. She said Lisa had it coming. My dad had to take a walk, he was so mad."

The voices trailed off.

So, now Lisa knew two things: 1. He was staying at some cabin without a car, 2. Don't trust his mother.

She thought about how to trick TJ into giving away the directions to the cabin. She mulled it over while Algebra wound its way through plus and minuses, while doing jumping jacks in P.E, while the frog in Bio lay splayed open on her dissecting tray, and finally decided to meet T.J. when he came out of Physical Science, which was just across the hall at the end of the day.

She got up when the bell rang and watched as bodies buffeted off each other as if a moving herd of wild animals. She caught a glimpse of TJ and called his name.

"Hey Adams!" She said with a smile. She liked this kid. He was unlike Jed in so many ways. He had a huge heart and she saw his compassion first hand when he spent time with his beloved dog Astro.

"Lisa! What's up? I am so sorry about the other day with Jed. You okay?"

"Nothing can take this old girl down. My hair has never been softer!" They laughed. "Hey TJ, I have some things that belong to Jed and I really need to return them in person. Do you know where he is after school?"

TJ looked down at his feet. Now, I've struck a nerve, Lisa thought.

"I do. But he made me promise not to tell anyone," TJ said in a low voice. "I have his car."

"I get it," Lisa said. "My dad grounded ME last night for being even involved with him. I sure wish I could just tell him to leave me alone."

"TJ!" Someone yelled, "Are you sure about not wanting 3:30 free burgers?

Lisa looked at TJ "Why not go with your friends? I can drive the car to him, finish up there, and get to tennis practice by 5:00 PM. We are doing the late one tonight."

"TEEEJ!" His friend yelled.

He dug into his pocket and threw her the keys. "He's going to be so pissed off at me," he said. "But I am so sick of having to babysit him. Let me draw you a quick map to the cabin. It's not too far."

After school, as she was walking out, Lisa looked around for Lynn. Come to think of it, she hadn't seen her in school all day. If there was something wrong, she's sure she would have heard. She got into Jed's black Chevy Chevelle and looked around the car. Nothing seemed out of the ordinary. Sinking low in the seat, she waited for after school traffic to clear. When the last cars left, followed by the buses, she went around to the trunk. Using the key on the ring, she opened it up.

Well, you had to give Jed kudos on neatness. Inside were a few newspaper bits and some sand or gravel, but things seemed pretty regular. She was just about to bring the trunk lid down, when there was a glimmer of something wedged up near the seam closest to the rear window. Brightly colored little circles that looked like candy. Reaching in she tried to wrest the candy pieces from deep in the seam of the fabric covering the spare.

It looked like someone had spilled an M & M bag in the trunk. Time was getting away. She shut the trunk and got back in the driver's seat. She gunned the engine and headed first to Lynn's.

The door was unlocked, so she opened it as she stood out near the stoop.

"Lynn? You home?" She yelled.

"She's not here yet." Lynn's sister, Eva, came into the kitchen and talked through the screen.

"Do you know if she had something after school?" Lisa asked, hating to waste the time with this girl who never had liked her.

"I don't know." Eva said.

"Okay. Thank you," Lisa said and flew back down the steps.

Putting the keys in the ignition, she couldn't shake the fact that there was candy in the trunk. It was really bugging her now. How could candy be wedged so far into the trunk? You could throw a bag in and maybe they'd spill out loosely. But she knew Jed, he loved his junk food. She couldn't imagine him leaving one M&M. Plus, why hadn't they melted? Knowing the clock was ticking, the lure of undoing the puzzle in the trunk got the best of her. She knew her brain. If something was giving her an itch, it would be best to scratch it right now and get it over with. Opening the trunk one more time she was thankful for the better lighting.

At first all she could see was the blank trunk. Had the candy been imagined? What did it matter? But focusing on finding color contrasts to the dark gray interior trunk, her eyes adjusted. Lifting up a loose flap she discovered many of the colorful

M&Ms. Why do I feel like I need to clean this up for him? She thought, reaching in and gathering all the pieces she could see. It was funny that they were all in the same spot. If someone had thrown a bag or handful in, they would be everywhere. The first one she picked up left a shock. This wasn't candy! It was a bead. There were at least seven that she could gather. Her brain was flashing a red alert: You have seen these before. Think!

It hit her so hard she sat down on the curb. These were hair beads. The girl at the old frame factory had them in her hair. The girl who ran. The girl who was found out at the fishing shack. The dead girl.

"Evidence!" She whispered to herself.

She placed the beads in an envelope she found in her purse and decided to show Bobby later. Right now time was of the essence. Artie had no idea there were two full hours between school and practice today, and she had to hope he was too busy at work to check up on her.

Lisa got the map out of her bag. She knew that TJ had been hasty, but it was easy enough to follow. Blue Star Highway had many country roads that fed into it. She headed north for a couple miles and then cut in toward the lake. The road was gravel and the plants on either side had overgrown it in spots. They formed an arch that became darker and more overgrown as it wound to the bluff. Finally, the densely shrouded undergrowth got in the way of the car's progress. Lisa parked the car halfway down the road and followed what appeared to be a path.

She saw it then. A little building. It was not much bigger than a shed. All the screens were torn on the porch and they flapped in the breeze. Garbage cluttered the entry as she stepped onto the porch and peered in. Her eyes adjusted to see an assortment of beer cans, old motor oil tins, rusted tools, a flea bitten mattress, a blanket, a hank of chain….

Stop. What did not fit in this picture?

Lisa went over to the mattress and squatted next to it to get a closer look. There was nothing to tell her if someone had lain on it recently. Tufts of stuffing were spilling out and it was dirty and crawling with bugs. Bugs? They were outdoor bugs. Slugs and wormlike insects that really favored dark moist dirt. Her foot nudged the mattress. There was a wet spot on the porch floor underneath it.

This mattress had been moved inside recently. It smelled wet and earthy. But she recognized the blanket. It was the one that Jed's mother made him and he usually kept it in his car. They used it for their picnic. Jed wouldn't lay on this mattress though, no matter how tired he was, she thought. It is gross. How puzzling to find the blanket left here on this porch.

She peeked in the open door. If Jed was expecting a ride from TJ, he sure didn't act like it. It looked like he'd had a few cans of Coke and some packages of Hostess Cupcakes; so very like him to be eating crap for food. The single room had little in it except a straight backed chair and a Playboy. Lisa shuddered to think what had gone on in here. Once again, thanking the stars for refusing him sex when he pushed to take the relationship to the next level.

There were the sounds of crackling twigs and she watched as the dried foliage parted. It revealed Jed, tall and still handsome, dragging an old rolled rug. He looked like he was having a struggle with that thing. It must be heavy, Lisa thought as she saw the sweat beads running down his face. He saw his car down the lane and yelled,

"TJ! Come and help me put this in the car. I got a deer!"

Lisa made up her mind to face him even though she knew the move was impulsive.

"TJ couldn't make it, Jed. So, I came to pick you up." She said "Surprise!"

Jed stopped dead in his tracks. He was exerting so much effort with the deer in the rug that he had to stand still a few seconds to process what and who was talking to him.

"Why the fuck are you even here? He asked "I have tried to keep you out of it." His jaw was moving even though his teeth were clenched tightly.

"Keep me out of it? What are you talking about? Here let me give you a hand." She walked over and reached around the rug and tugged.

"Get the fuck away from her," he said.

"Her?" Lisa said "What do you mean her? Who is in that rug?"

She raced over and wrestled the rug out of his hands. Bending over, she pushed hard with her foot.

Oh God! Oh God! She was breathing hard as the rug took its time unfurling.

An arm plopped out of the rug. It was brown and dirty but she saw the ring right away. It had been Lynn's grandmother's. It was her most prized possession and she never took it off.

"Jed! You finally pulled off what I couldn't!" Lisa exclaimed, "I have been trying to get this girl out of my life for the past year! Do you know I am the laughing stock at the yacht club having a black girl that I pal around with? Man! They almost didn't let me on the golf course last spring because I brought her along."

"I thought she was your best friend!" He cried, "your little black girlfriend who would never reveal your secrets."

Lisa forced a laugh.

"Did you really believe I would actually tell her my secrets? I haven't seen her for at least a week! My family has forbidden her from my house," Lisa exclaimed, hoping Lynn could not hear her words.

"But Jed, why is she here?" She asked tentatively. "What is she even doing here?"

Jed ignored her questions.

"Well, since I know your feelings, it makes my life better," he said "Hell! I would never have poured that tray of food on you if I had known. You snubbed me hard in front of Sadie. That wasn't cool."

"I am so sorry that I had that meeting. My grades are slipping and Mrs. Dallie wanted to meet with me or she'd tell my parents."

Jed was looking at her with one eye squinted. "You could have told me," He said. "I thought you wanted to break up."

"Break up? I love you so much. I had to pretend to break up so they'd get off my back."

He swooped her up into her arms and kissed her passionately. She wanted to gag. It was a survivor moment.

"Look. Lynn is just out cold for now. I am supposed to hand her over to some friends who will take her far away from here. But I have to get her in my trunk and head into town to pick up directions."

"I'll help!" She exclaimed complacently. "Where are we going?"

"*We* aren't going anywhere. I am going to drop you off at practice. Isn't it your late night? And I can come back and pick you up."

"Um, there's no practice tonight," she said. "They're fixing the courts."

He leaned over and kissed her hard.

"Maybe now you have time to deliver on some real loving'" He said, stroking her leg.

"If only," She said.

"If only what?" Jed's voice was filled with huskiness.

"If only I wasn't grounded," Lisa said.

"Well, at least it's something to look forward to." He was taking her hand and rubbing it across the zipper of his jeans. "I want you to feel how much I want that."

"Mm," Lisa tried to look dreamy but she was in the middle of a nightmare! "Listen, though. I have time to ride with you now because my dad thinks I am at practice. Maybe after we deliver...we can...?"

What was she proposing? Her brain was racing. She just had to stay with Lynn in this car.

He made it to the post office without bursting out of his pants. She was sure he was going to unzip and make something happen. But he told her to wait there, and he looked directly at her when he took the keys from the ignition.

Aw, Shit.

She thought about running next door to the library to use their phone but she knew she just didn't have time because he was already coming back.

He approached the car.

"Ok. Looks like the drop is in Hastings. You can't come. I asked."

"Oh too bad," she said as her hand went to his thigh "Who are these lame people who tell you what to do?"

"Just the same person who has controlled my whole life," he answered, looking deeply into her eyes. "I need to come right back so you can know how very much I adore you. Where can we meet?"

Lisa thought fast. She had to think of a place and alert Bobby Washington. Where could she go to make him think that she was in the mood for love?

"I know. Let's meet at Maple Street Beach. You know, at Murdock's old beach house. You can get in through the back door."

"I know right where that is," he said. "I'll park my car in the little grocery store lot. The store's closed for the season but the lot's open. It's not a long walk."

"Okay. Let me out here," she said looking around the parking lot of the post office. "There's hardly anyone around."

"Where are you going now?" Jed asked, concerned.

"To the drug store and then the beach, silly," she said, trying to flirt. "My first time is going to be special."

He grinned and puffed out his chest.

"I am already ready," he said, grabbing her hand to touch him again. "But you're right, it is a special time."

She opened the door and blew him a kiss. As he pulled away, she memorized his license plate number.

Five full minutes passed as she gave him ample time to turn right at the light and head up to the highway. She wished she had more details than just Hastings. On the way to the drugstore, she crossed the street and went behind the tire parts store. She checked the parking lot between the store and the fire station. Since Heaven was such a small town, the police and fire stations were housed in the same building. She looked for the light blue Camaro. It was there!

Rushing inside the door, she stopped at the front desk. Everyone knew who she was. She used to like the idea, but now it would be hard to hide the fact that she had been at the police station.

"Is Officer Washington available?" She asked breathlessly.

The sour looking chick they had as a receptionist gave her a once over. Lisa recognized her as one of the Sackett twins. The one that got pregnant on prom night two years ago. As she stood, Lisa noticed her sagging belly. Her thighs and butt had spread. She had the distinctive tired face of someone stuck in a hopeless place. It looked like she gained 40 years and 40 pounds.

Bobby Washington gave her a pensive look as he walked around the front desk.

"Lisa?" He said her name with a question mark.

"I need to talk to you and we need to move fast," she said.

"Let's step into the conference room," he said as he gently pushed her forward. "Too many eyes."

Once inside the conference room he shut the door and faced her.

"Tell me everything you know. Don't stop."

"Lynn is in trouble. Jed Adams is taking her to Hastings in *the trunk of his car*. He plans to hand her over to some people there who will "take her far away from here." He is driving a black Chevy Chevelle with a Michigan plate: JAS127. He left about 15 minutes ago."

"Ok. Hold up." He reached over to the black phone and lifted the receiver. Several buttons lit up. He pressed one and asked for Commander Dan Johnson. He spoke in jargon she didn't quite understand. APB. Armed and Dangerous. Assailant/ victim. But when he finished he said:

"Okay. We will pick him up on his way to Hastings. He will go to the State Police Post. Now, say he slips through our fingers, are there any other details?"

"He thinks I still want to be with him. I am supposed to meet him at Maple Street Beach later; at Murdock's old beach house. It's supposed to be locked up."

"Well, where are you supposed to be now, because if I know your dad, this isn't the place?"

"I have tennis practice. It started like ten minutes ago. I was just going to skip it."

"Actually, I think that that might be the best place for you. I will drop you off. Come on!"

"But Bobby? How will I know about Lynn? How will I know she is okay?" She was starting to feel all the held back emotions begin to press forward. Don't crack now, she told herself.

"Look. At this very moment, there are state police and FBI agents combing the highways and back roads for his car. They will find him."

"No matter what, I want to know what is happening'" she told him.

"You have my word," he said.

Lisa

Late practice was the easiest. Coach Jan was so laid back, all they did was hit the ball and practice the strokes she said to practice. You: Take forehand. You: Take backhand. You: Practice your serve. There was no organization. Out of the corner of her eye, Lisa caught sight of an orange Cadillac with a tan vinyl roof. That would be her dad. She waved as she watched him pull into the parking space.

"Wow. Your dad is keeping an eye on you." Kim said, stating the obvious.

"Yeah. I guess I am grounded for what happened in the cafeteria the other day." Lisa answered ,"You know because I got hot, goopy food poured on me."

"You were quite a sight. So many people were mad," Kim replied.

"But, yet no one stepped in, how convenient." Lisa felt snarky.

"That is one crazy mother." Kim went on, "Everyone knows he's up to no good. Hell, the principal was in there at the speed of light. Like he knew it was going to happen."

"Ha. Lucky me! Well, I am heading out. Coach, I have to go." Lisa gestured to the coach that she was leaving.

Coach smiled and waved. She heard about the incident in the lunchroom and then how Lisa's boyfriend had been suspended. She chose to not get personally involved in her players' lives.

Lisa decided to go home, but she by-passed Artie's car and walked onto the sidewalk. She was really beat. The emotional toll was adding up. As she walked, she thought about what a mistake all this stuff with Jed Adams had been. She'd never let a man dominate her again. But that was laughable, for here was her dad slowly idling behind her.

"Get in the car," he said. "It's time we talked."

Reluctantly, she threw her things in his trunk. There was a clang when her bag landed on an oil can. Crap. That gun was still in there. She had forgotten all about it.

"I apologize for grounding you," her father began. "If I had known what a piss ant that kid was I would never have let you go out with him. I did some looking into his background. He's no good. You have to stay far away from him."

"I know dad. I'm trying. But I think he's hurt my friend." She started crying.

"Who, Sadie? Chrissie? Jennifer? You just tell me. I will kick his little ass."

"Her name is Lynn, dad. Lynn Parris?'

"You mean that colored girl? Her brother plays football with Billy?"

"She's black, dad. Yes. She's my friend. She has a hard working mother. They go to church on Sundays. They go to their grand-parents in the country. They are happy and joyful and I love being around them! They are like us in many ways except they don't try to constantly put other people down or judge. I hope you can see your way clear to have an open mind."

"What? You don't think I have black friends?" He asked. "I have so many."

"Okay dad. But think about the Heavenly Country Club, the yacht club. Any black members? Are they even allowed in? Do you know any black people who own businesses?"

"What about Booker Drysdale?" He asked. "I bring my dad around there every summer for them to talk about tailoring."

"Yes you do," Lisa said. "I just wish this town was a little more modern. Like, not caring who was friends with who. I mean, there are white people here that I wouldn't trust, with a ten foot pole, like I do Lynn."

Her father gave her a long look. He saw her as his beautiful, naive girl. Her long, shiny hair, the color of midnight, was falling out of her hair tie. Wisps of it stuck to her face. Of all things in his life, his family came first. In keeping them up on the pedestal, sometimes they were out of his personal reach. Lisa beseeched him to take a look at how they lived. He was trying to push beyond his South Side Chicago roots his entire life. Now, he discovered, maybe he pushed too far the other way. He decided to give his daughter his viewpoint on life's pecking order.

"You know, no one hands you anything in life," he began. "I don't purposely shun black people as friends. I have many casual ones. I guess I have always been trying to make it up my own ladder. Even though I came from the Chicago area, I had to fight for every job or award I was given. My father came from Italy as a young man. Back in those days, Italians were treated little better than black people are now. My right hand to God, if I ever have considered myself anything but a hustler for my family. I was the only one in my family to go to college. I had to work while at school because the scholarship for football only covered tuition and books. My friends were mostly Italian or immigrant sons like me. My theory is people should hang out with who they are comfortable with. People who make them feel good."

"Dad. I love you. But that's such a safe answer," Lisa said. "Nobody puts down their blinders for one second in this town to see all the people that live here. We all ignore if someone sees us together with people that don't fit in. You know Billy goes to parties in the Zone? He does, dad. Do you think that's wrong? I want more for my life. I want people to quit whispering. I want people to know that having acquaintances and having friends are not the same thing. They just aren't. In this town, everyone's so judgmental. I would rather go to a party with Lynn than my other friends. She is real. She gets who I am."

"Then I would say you are lucky. Not many people can say that about any of their friends, regardless of the color. The world takes its time turning, and I think people just have to be comfortable with themselves. You know. Jesus said, "Know thyself." I think we have a lot of fake robots around here."

They were turning down the street when a Michigan State Police car, with a red light flashing on top, passed them on the left and sped down their short block. Lisa squeezed her eyes shut. She thought the car might not be able to stop and would fly over the lake bank like a scene from *Starsky and Hutch*.

It did stop. It was right in front of her house. She looked over at her dad.

"Dad! What's happening?" She screamed. But he didn't answer. He got out of the car and walked to the squad car.

"Artie Palma?"

The strange policeman got out of the car.

"Yes." Her father stood very still as if taking mental count of who was home and who was not.

"Your son, Billy, has been involved in an incident. He is okay but they are holding him at the station. Seems the entire football team was involved. We'll fill you in if you can come with us."

Lisa's dad looked over at her.

"Tell your mother to keep all the other kids home. I will bring Billy back as soon as this is all sorted out."

Lisa looked at the officer. "Sir? Do you know Bobby Washington?"

The cop just looked at her.

What the hell was going on? She thought.

Lynn

Her head was pulsating with each heartbeat. In and out of sleep, Lynn felt like those first few days of school when your body tells you to sleep in another ten minutes. Thankfully, I am not tied up, she thought. I am as snug as a bug in a rug. She had discerned this earlier. This crazy mother fucker was taking her somewhere again! She was in a damn car trunk.

My poor mama, she thought. You must be worried sick. By now she would have told Lamar to go out and look for me. I hope she has contacted Bobby too. If I wasn't so sleepy…

Minutes passed and the jostling of the car eased. They were driving more slowly. The trunk popped open and Jed Adams stuck his head inside.

"I hope you are still with me, Lynn." He said "I want to get you cleaned up and out of that rug." He was grunting as he heaved the rug, with her still inside, to the road. After unrolling it, he had her sit up. He reached over and brought out a boy scout canteen that he stole from one of his stupid stepbrothers.

"Get some water in you," he said. "And take a pee break."

She looked around. They were in the middle of two corn fields. The corn had long since been harvested, but no one had been around to plant. It was too early for that. Lynn walked slowly. She was dizzy. She doubted she could make a break for it even if she was in better shape.

"Jed. You know me." She said ,"I am a good person. Can't you see your way clear to let this all go? How do you think Lisa will feel when she finds out what you've done?"

He laughed.

"You don't even know what I've done." He said smiling. "Your friend loves me more than she does you."

The silence was split in two by a roar that arose from the wooded area on either side of the corn lots. Engines! Dust was being kicked up by the tires of so many cars that it seemed like they were at the Motor Speedway. The cars surrounded Lynn and Jed. Things were happening so fast. In the blink of an eye, the drivers were out of their cars. Some had chains. Others brandished aluminum softball ball bats. There were snarls of ropes and weight lifting weights-things that could be found in most garages. The drivers had their hats pulled down low, but Lynn began to see a commonality. All over the clothes and even on some of the sports equipment was the logo for their high school: a halo with wings. This stuff came from the Heavenly Saints locker room!

Lynn looked closer. There were people here that she knew. She was shocked to see Lisa's brother Billy with a golf club. Her eyes got wide when she saw the leader. It was Lamar! He didn't hide himself but strode up to Jed and put his face right up to his.

"Now, how is it you are out here in the middle of nowhere with my sister?" He snarled. The group began to close in. Lynn was put inside a car, as the young high school athletes began to take their revenge out on Jed. Each time a weapon hit home, a crush or an oomph would be uttered. It might have taken all of five minutes. Lamar signaled to the group.

"No. Man. We are bringing his ass in alive."

He got in the car.

"Lynn. When this is all over, I'm going to whoop you too. But maybe not so hard."

"Lamar! How did you know to come out here? Who told you?"

"Like you don't know." Lamar said, "Bobby Washington told me where you'd be and he gave me a ten minute head start. I figure the cops will be taking care of the rest of this problem. Bobby wanted more, though. More than the police would give. He is still a brother from the 'hood. He sure is sweet on you, Lynn."

"Good Lord!" Lynn murmured. "How did you get all these boys out here?"

"All I had to do is ask," Lamar said "When one of Heaven's people is in trouble, we rise up together."

"Is Mama okay?" She asked.

"She will be, Baby Sister. She will be. She thinks I got mixed up with the Black Disciples," he laughed. "She has no idea what our high school boys can do when one of our own is threatened. These guys don't mind a little rumble now and again."

"But they are high school students, Lamar!" She looked over at the unmoving Jed Adams, his body covered in dust and blood. "They are going to have to explain all this."

"We got it all covered. It's cool," Lamar said.

Lynn looked at her brother. He seemed to have grown into a man overnight. Self-assured and confident, he knew what he had done was for the right reasons.

"Start walking back toward the road, Lynn. The police probably have caught up by now." Lamar was signaling his group to "huddle up."

Lisa

Pacing in the front yard caught the attention of Sadie. She walked up the street to stand in front of Lisa's house. They had not been on very good terms since that doughnut day. Sadie had a secret to tell Lisa.

"Hey, are you all right"? She asked. "I haven't talked to you for eons."

"I just have a lot of stuff going on," Lisa said dismissively.

"Look," Sadie said. "That day that we caught a ride home with Jed, well, um, he came back and we went out riding around. I didn't mean to do anything with him. We just kissed."

Well, that didn't take long, Lisa thought. Probably needed some insurance in case she didn't come around.

"I didn't plan on making it permanent," Sadie said, chastened. "My mother got wind of him coming over and she said no way should I hang out with him." She looked up quickly. "Not that I have even planned to. My mom says she remembers his father from high school. Did you know his father was black?"

"Well, your mom is right about one thing. Stay away from him. He is not a good person."

"I told him I couldn't go out with him at all, and he got all mad. How did you ever stand it?"

"Obviously, not very well. I am grounded until next year probably," Lisa groaned.

"What's with all the police cars around?"

"There was a break in at my dad's office," Lisa said, lying easily. "That's all I know."

The unmistakable light blue Camaro just turned into the neighborhood. Lisa looked at Sadie.

"You better go back home," she said. "I will fill you in on all this later."

She did not want Sadie to have any news at all. Not yet.

"Hey Bobby!" Sadie said, not moving from her spot. "What's with all the police traffic around here?"

Lisa stood frozen. Please don't get her involved, she pleaded bulging her eyes out. But Bobby was smooth.

"Well, if I told ya I'd have to kill ya." He chuckled. "Just making sure everyone's safe."

Realizing that was it for any information, Sadie dawdled a few seconds longer, then turned and walked home.

"Sadie had a hot moment with Jed." Lisa told Bobby when Sadie was out of ear shot.

"Good to know. I'll walk down there later. Give her mother a chance to spaz out," Bobby said.

Watching her go, Lisa stuck her head inside the car.

"What's happened?" She asked, "Did you find her?"

"We did find her. But the plan has gone off the rails," Bobby was agitated.

"What do you mean, off the rails? You found her, right?"

"I need to talk to your mother," He said as he opened the door and tediously got out of the car. He was a big man, and unfolding his six foot five frame from the car was more of a contortionist's act.

"I got to get a bigger car," He laughed.

Carla Palma had been watching out the window of the family room like a little bird at the feeder. She wanted to see more but kept well back behind the curtain. It was a well-or-chestrated spying maneuver and usually worked for neighbors and stray cars.

"Bobby," Her mother said as she opened the door and let them into the family room.

"Hello Mrs. Palma. Billy's fine and this isn't about him. I was wondering if you had seen a burgundy Cadillac around here lately. It is a newer model with Illinois plates.

Lisa looked at Bobby. He didn't know where the Cadillac was.

"Our neighbor in back just bought a burgundy Cadillac at Becker's."

"Well, well, well. Is he back there now?" Bobby asked.

"I just got back from there. His place has finally sold and he is boxing up things tonight. But Officer Washington, let me go with you. Poor Bob is so easily excited."

"Thank you. That would help tremendously?" Bobby said.

"Let me get my jacket," Lisa's mother said. When Carla went to the closet Bobby leaned over to Lisa and said,

"There is something else." He paused and as his words hung there in the air.

"Gilbert Morse is conscious and talking."

Lisa took a sharp intake of air. This story was not over. Everyone knew that Gilbert's drug use made him a very accomplished liar when it came to telling stories of woe. If he needed money, he could make one up on a dime.

"I just want to bring you into the station to make a statement on what you saw that involved Gilbert. Because, I am afraid, with no gun found on the scene of William Langley's murder, we are going to have to release him."

"She is not going anywhere with you." Carla spoke now with the vengeance of a mother lion. "I will wait for her father to get home and then we will have time to figure this out."

"Mrs. Palma, he already gave me the okay," Bobby said. "You should be getting a call anytime."

She marched inside and looked at the phone. The receiver was not hung up. In fact, she could see the extra-long, coiled phone line went under the door of the closet.

"Who has this phone in the closet?" She cried. She opened the door to find the twins curled up fast asleep with the phone receiver in Timmy's lap. "Oh sweet Jesus!" She screamed as she took the phone and hung it in its cradle. It rang instantly.

"I am sorry. I know. Well, the boys had it in the closet. He's here now. Uh huh. Uh huh. Oh my. Okay."

Artie must be having a heart attack over there, Lisa thought.

"Okay," Carla said. "Take her with you. Artie will be waiting for a word from you."

"This could take a while, Carla," Bobby said. "Please tell your neighbor I will need him to come into the station with that

Cadillac tonight, if possible."

Lisa walked with Bobby to the car. She saw Sadie watching through her fence. It was woven like a basket with large boards painted white and made for privacy between the two lots. George Like was the owner of the house next door to Sadie's. In fact, he owned most of the property on Baver Court. too. His own home, with the tar paper siding and fake shingled brick front walls was an eyesore. Dogs were chained to dog sheds in the back and she knew Sadie's father went to the Heaven City Board several times to have them removed. George didn't take care of his house. There was no lawn and it really belonged a street over, although it seemed like he got satisfaction from keeping it a shit hole out of spite. The thing was, there was no way to get rid of his place. He was a slum lord to the renters on Baver Court and probably had more liquid capital than the other members of the entire block.

"Okay, Lisa. I am going to talk and you are going to listen," Bobby began. "Gilbert Morse is awake, that's true. But he was so messed up that day, he thought that it was Benny Forter that beat him up, and shot him and William."

"Who is Benny Forter? Why does that name sound familiar?" Lisa asked.

"Well, as of last week, he owned a burgundy Cadillac." Bobby answered.

"Jed's real dad! That's right," Lisa whispered. "Bobby, I have something to tell you." Lisa was trembling. "Lynn found a handgun out on 16th Street. She thinks it's the one the police were looking for."

Bobby's eyes got darker.

"She what?" He asked, "Damn! You girls just keep making my job harder."

"But I have it. She gave it to me the night she thought we were getting more information on the beach. We thought we needed it for protection."

He turned to her.

"Where is it?" He asked.

"It's in my gym bag," Lisa answered.

"All right, that's it!" Bobby growled. "Bring me that gun so we can get it checked out."

Lisa had never seen Bobby so mad. Truth be told, she and Lynn gave him way more clues about this case than he would have gotten on his own. Her own blood started to boil. If he would just get the job done, all the people out there stealing and hurting kids could be stopped. At least for a while.

Her bag was in her room. She went inside through the garage. The ranch style house had been added on to several times. When they built the garage and the upstairs addition, the boys and her parents took the new bedrooms up the stairs. Her parent's old bedroom became a sort of mudroom and passageway from the lower level to the upper one. It was also an entrance room from the garage. She ran through the backroom and grabbed her bag. She took the whole thing back out to the Camaro.

By now, neighbors were gathering at Ellis' lot between their house and Palma's. Seeing Lisa get in the car with Bobby Washington was troubling to them. The entire group was getting bits and pieces of the rumble north of town. Many of the football team members were being released and coming home. But Bobby was out of uniform. Was she cavorting with a man of color right in front of her parents?

"Bobby, can we do this somewhere else?" Lisa asked. "I mean, my neighbors are going to make up so many stories."

"Show me the gun," he said.

She reached in and brought out the gun in its plastic bag covering.

"Have you or Lynn touched this thing?"

"It's possible it was touched but we tried to be careful," Lisa answered.

Bobby grabbed a large cloth bag marked EVIDENCE and placed the gun inside. He was quiet.

"Okay. Look. I'll be honest with you. This man, Benny Forter, is a big king pin in smuggling kids to places all over the world. I have been studying him for a long time and he seems to have the most success with black communities. You would be surprised how many folks just quit looking after a week or two. He is a terrible man. The saddest part is, your boyfriend has been tied up with him for quite a while."

"He's not my boyfriend," Lisa said quickly. "He has a mean streak. I already know. You don't think he would have smuggled me somewhere, do you?"

"If he ever hurt or threatened you and wanted you to keep secrets? Why, that's what they start out like. Love you one minute, beating the stuffing out of you the next, or worse. I am sorry to be insensitive with you, but did he ever…I mean, um, well the sex part is a part of the process too."

"No sex. I promised maybe tonight would be the first time. But I was hoping you would catch him before I had to meet him. I mean, Bobby, he shot that little girl. I have the beads from his trunk in my purse."

"You what?" Bobby ran a hand over his face. "Can you bring them to me?"

"Yes, if you quit acting like I am hiding them or something," she said.

"Well, believe it or not, William had already started grooming Lynn," Bobby said. "She was too ashamed to let anyone know about Gilbert, for fear Zenobia will find out. I need to get to her and you can help. They dropped her off at the ER and we will go there first. Her mother is with her, so let's keep all the inside information on the Q.T."

"What an asshole," Lisa remarked. "And the Cadillac? Aren't you going to look inside?"

"Well, since you found the beads, I don't have to."

Lynn

It made Lynn feel like a queen the way all the athletes came to her rescue. It almost made up for the past few days. Her fears of never being pretty, or liked, or thought about vanished into thin air. These boys were from all walks of life. They were sons of factory workers, bankers, and merchants in town. Many of them would never even say hello to her in the hallway at school, but Lamar led the crusade and she could tell he felt validated as well.

The emergency entrance to Heaven's only hospital was a covered turnaround at the curb on Bailey Street. Usually pretty quiet, there was certainly an uproar this evening. Reporters from newspapers all over the area were there with cameras. Two State of Michigan police cars blocked the E.R. drive. When Pat Kelly, a big bruiser of a center at 230 pounds, got out and asked the cops for assistance, Lynn watched the reporters look at him and then immediately converge on her in the car. Shouting through the windows and popping flashbulbs, Lynn felt that she would never get to be just Lynn Parris again.

"Back the Hell up!" Boomed a voice through a handheld loudspeaker. "You will be given a statement at the front entrance in 15 minutes. But for now, move out of this area."

Lynn looked to the source of the commanding voice. She knew it before she saw him. It belonged to Bobby. She opened the door but Pat Kelly shut it again. He held up a pointer finger indicating she needed to wait. The crowd of reporters was thinning. Soon, the Heaven Police were setting up cones across the E.R. driveway. The automatic doors opened with a whoosh and two orderlies, decked out in paper scrubs, came around to her door. They would not let her even get in a wheelchair, but whisked her up on a gurney and bumped her up the curb and into the hospital.

Her mother was the first person she saw. What a horrible week for her, Lynn thought. But when she got close, her mother smiled at her warmly.

"The Lord answered my prayer bringing you back to me, Baby Girl. No matter what has happened to you, I will always love you deeply."

"Mama! I am so sorry to have upset you. I guess I think I am invincible sometimes." Lynn's eyes were misting over.

"Well, you look a sight!" Zenobia laughed. "But I would recognize my girl any day. Even under 100 coats of mud!"

Lynn saw Bobby and Lisa come through the E.R. doors. She didn't even care if Bobby saw her like this. She was dizzy with relief that for now, she and Lisa were safe.

"Doctor Willman's going to look you over," Mama said. "I will wait right here."

Lynn's eyes locked with Bobby. His eyes were wrinkling at the corner. She knew he was in his 20s still. That put her maybe, five years behind him in age. It was doable.

Lisa's face showed a level of concern. They had to decompress, she knew.

"I am okay. Don't be worried. I heard he was in here too."

Lisa looked at Bobby. If Jed Adams was in a room somewhere, maybe she should go and talk to him; pry some more information out of him. A small part of her really wanted to know he was okay. But Bobby knew the loyalty that abused people had for their abusers. Just last year, a woman came into the station. She had just fled from her boyfriend in the middle of an argument, after it had gotten physical. He knew the couple well, as the Heaven Police were called out to their house at least every few weeks on domestic assault calls. Each time, the boyfriend was removed from the premises. But the woman always took him back. It was all part of a multi-layered codependency. In the end, after at least seven calls and reunions she broke it off for good from a hospital bed.

Although Lisa had not been going out with Jed Adams long, he had been able to beat her, break up, and return several times. Lynn told Bobby of her concerns about Lisa. She tended to wobble when Jed wanted to get back together, promising to never hurt her again. Bobby found it puzzling that Lisa had not confided in her father sooner. He knew Artie had a temper, everyone knew, although he had never been called to handle abuse or anything. Maybe she was hiding one from the other, so as not to make them mutually worse. But Bobby was also concerned for Lynn. Her abuse had been in mental form from William. One of keeping secrets that made her feel worthless. Both girls were going to need more than the high school counselor to figure this out.

"No. Nope. Nada," Bobby said as he read Lisa's mind. "You don't need to go there. He is not up to seeing visitors. Even his mother has been asked to stay away. He is in police custody."

They wheeled Lynn away, and Lisa put her face in her hands and wept. Zenobia came over to her and quietly rubbed her back. She felt the need to nurture someone in her own time of uncertainty. She leaned over and whispered in Lisa's ear:

"You know, this is not your fault. There is no way I will ever be able to thank you for saving Lynn. William was a no-good man. I should have known, Lord, I should have known. Now we can put this all behind us and start walking on two sure feet."

"I am so sorry Lynn had to take so much," Lisa said. "I feel as if they targeted her because of me."

"Do you think they weren't already getting her to that point?" Zenobia cried. "I know what happened with Gilbert Morse. I know that William set it up. He just made it look like he was surprised."

"How can you even know that?" Lisa asked.

"Because men who know their days are numbered, often try to come clean for their sins." Zenobia leaned back in her chair. "He has met the Maker already and I am pretty certain it was not good news."

Lisa looked at her, stunned. Zenobia knew and never comforted Lynn or had Gilbert arrested. She must have looked confused.

"Lisa," Zenobia said "I know you think it harsh of me for not doing more than praying for Gilbert Morse. But I come from a time where delicate matters like that are not shared with the public. I have not shared this with anyone but the Lord. He will judge Gilbert. Lynn is a strong girl. She will turn out just fine. You'll see. That is all I will say on the matter and I don't expect you to speak of it with Lynn."

Before she could reply, Lisa spotted a nurse with a starched hat and thick glasses coming toward them. She said, "Zenobia, you may go back. Bobby just went in to question her."

Lisa got up to go join Zenobia.

"Just her mother, right now." The nurse said gently to Lisa, "Can I bring you a Coke or something to drink?"

"Oh. No thank you," Lisa said with exasperation. The conversation with Lynn's mother was almost too much to bear, yet she knew it was coming from a place of love.

"I will just use the bathroom."

"There is one just down this hall." The nurse said pointing to the left.

"Thanks," Lisa said and she picked up her purse and coat and started down the hall.

Lisa

Heaven did not have more than one floor for inpatient care. Anything severe was taken straight away to Kalamazoo's two larger hospitals. Lisa took her time heading to the bathroom. There were pictures on the walls that were painted by kids who had stayed at the hospital. Framed and in a row at eye level, they were pretty good. A great way to cover a hospital wall, she thought. She looked from one to the next until she got to the next corridor. A nurse was coming out of a patient room.

"Boy, for the beating that guy took, it's hard to believe he is conscious," She said to the policeman staked out by the room.

"Come on and share a little of this cake." The nurse was still talking up the cop. He got up and moved to a spot behind the nurse's station. Lisa took this as a cue to slip into the room.

It was darkened and there were several machines beeping or blinking. Once her vision adjusted, she walked over to the bed. Jed's eyes were swollen nearly shut. His face had several spots where it had been sewn up, the gashes so wide, they barely met at the edges. Blood was beginning to crust around his nose. Lisa took a cloth and wet it. She gingerly cleaned what she could from his face. His arm was in a plaster cast and one leg was up in traction.

"Fancy meeting you here," Jed said, through voluminous lips. "I knew you would make sure I was alright. Because you know I didn't do anything wrong, right? You know I didn't put Lynn in any danger. I was just doing like I was told. She would have never been harmed. Ever. You know that, right?"

"Oh God, Jed," Lisa said. "Do you really think that is going to work anymore? You took my friend and you had every intention of taking me. I don't love you, because you don't know how to love. You just don't. I am just in here to take a look at what I finally was able to do to you."

"You say that now," he said. "But I willed you here and here you are."

All of a sudden, Lisa felt the smolder deep down in her gut start to flare. She wasn't here because she was under his power! Someone's ego is going to lose.

"Well, if I was here for you, would I do this? She asked as she untied the traction on his leg.

He bellowed in pain. She looked toward the nurse's station where the horny nurse and the hornier cop were blatantly flirting.

"I wonder if I was here for you if I would do this," She placed a pillow over his face. The rage was black and bubbling over. "Think I wouldn't?" Holding and pushing the pillow she had every intention of finishing him. An orderly walked by causing her to release the pillow. Jed was gasping for breath.

"If you ever come near me or send any of your goons or your crazy ass father, I will fuck you up like you could never imagine. Just try one more time, you sorry son of a bitch loser. I will not let up next time. Stay the hell away."

She ran out into the hall.

The machines began to light up and buzz. The cop popped up out of his seat so quickly that the spinning chair knocked the nurse over. A doctor, fresh to his shift, called:

"Hey? Is someone supposed to be with this patient? There's a whole bunch of noise coming from those machines!"

Lisa continued quickly down the hall.

A black orderly was mopping up the floor in the hall. She sidestepped his mop and nodded an 'excuse me.' The way he stood and turned to watch her made her very uneasy. His shoes squeaked on the wet floor. The noise drew her attention to his feet. He was wearing black boots buffed to a high shine.

Out-of-place! Out-of-place! Her brain began buzzing as loudly as the machines.

She made a mental note to review this later. She had to get out of there before anyone summoned Bobby or the detectives still wandering about. Walking fast, she went through the E.R. door and out of the hospital. It was very dark and she hung to the shoulder of the road as best she could. She hadn't stopped at Lynn's room. Just knowing that both she and Jed were in the same hospital with only a hallway between them was cause for concern. But Bobby would stay. She knew. He would take care of Lynn for now.

Lynn

"Bobby, I am not spending the night here. I know Jed is down that hallway and there is no way. He is a very dangerous person."

"Lynn," Bobby said softly, "I doubt that that boy can lift a finger to harm you in his present state. Don't worry. We are just going to wait for test results, and then if they are good we will take you home."

"Bobby! Do you ever not work?" Lynn asked, "Please take my mother home. If you are sure nothing will happen to me here. I am so sleepy. I need to take a little nap and I bet these tests will take a while."

"Yeah, not a bad idea. I need to check in at the station. Your mother could use some rest," Bobby said. He was concerned about Zenobia too. "I will be back within the hour."

He found Lynn's mother in the waiting room curled up in a tiny ball. She was fast asleep.

"Zenobia," He said gently. "Let's get you home."

"Where's my girl?" She asked.

"I will take care of you first and then come back and get her," Bobby said. "There are people all over the place to make sure she's safe."

"Oh, how did I get so lucky to have you in my world, son? You have been such a dear friend." Zenobia said with a weary smile. "Maybe someday I can talk you into marrying one of my girls…"

"Well, that would surely be something," Bobby said wondering if he was going overboard for this family. In many ways they had been there for him through his boyhood struggles. Zenobia always had a plate of hot food and a warm smile for him.

Tossing her third empty Snack Pak pudding cup on the tray with a metallic clang, Lynn was starting to lose her patience. She read and re-read the words on the label over and over. Putting them in different languages she faintly remembered from her grandfather. The commercial circulated in her brain. It was a sign of the times. All groups were represented. Four kids were sitting on a baseball bench. There were two white boys, a black boy, and a girl. The boy who brought the pudding was white. Lynn mused wondering what would have happened if the black child had brought the pudding. Did it matter to the company's overall earnings? The lids on these containers were razor sharp and she remembered Luann Haniville cut the top of her pinkie finger clean off trying to open one. The ads on television began warning kids to "be very careful and don't cut yourself."

There was a knock at the door. It was well after midnight. The doctor strode in reeking of cigarette smoke. Nice that you could take a break while I am waiting here, Lynn thought.

"Well, Miss Parris. It looks like things have checked out in your favor. You are free to go home. You have most likely sustained a concussion and should be awakened through the night, every hour. Is there someone who can do that at your house?"

"On it." Bobby Washington volunteered as he rushed back into the room. "I will take her home and her mother has made me up a spot on the couch. I will wake her so that her mother can get some rest."

"Way above the call of duty," Lynn complained.

"I guess you will have to owe me," Bobby said.

When they got in the car, Bobby handed Lynn a cloth bag that had EVIDENCE stamped on it.

"It appears that the gun you found is not the murder weapon. I am probably a fool to do this, but I am giving it back to you. I will give you some easy lessons in shooting it."

Lynn looked stricken. "I don't like guns, Bobby."

"Look. I just want it by you. Slip it in the pocket of a coat that only you will wear. Find a place where the kids won't stumble on it by accident."

"Now I have heard everything!" Lynn hollered. "I will keep it in my stuffed animal with the zipper hide. No one would ever take that. But it will never be taken out, and this is stupid."

Bobby looked at her. "It's not like I want you to use it, but you need to be safe when I can't be there. There is no doubt in my mind that Benny Forter is dangerous and will be coming for you."

Lamar came to the hospital earlier. He and Bobby performed a special handshake. Lynn smiled. Her brother, whom she had always adored, had really come through for her. Hearing the details from the State Police report, no athlete was going to be charged with any misdemeanors. Bobby told Lamar it was a good thing they left off the beating when they did. If Jed had died, it would have been a different story. Lynn wondered what had become of her friend Lisa. It occurred to her that she hadn't seen her since being wheeled out of the waiting room.

"Bobby. You did take Lisa home, right?"

"Aw. Dammit. I knew I forgot something." Bobby shook his head. "I am sure someone was able to take her home. I really don't want to go over there now and check. I would wake up that entire household and it's late."

"Well, I am sure if her parents haven't called, she is probably okay,." Lynn said.

She got up quickly and the spinning in her head caused her to lay back down.

"Whoa," she said.

"You have to go slow," the doctor said. Bobby was quick to rush to her side. "Keeping you down might be a full time job," he chuckled. Lynn watched him through a fog. Beautiful white teeth. Handsome strong jawline. Strong solid arms.

She was sleeping before he wheeled her to the car. This is a special girl, he thought.

Lisa

As she passed the old armory, built in 1923, its darkened windows caused her to feel a chill, haunting her with their emptiness. She had a little further to go to be home, perhaps a mile, but the events of the day and the lateness of the hour were making each step feel as if she was lifting cement.

A car pulled up behind her.

"Miss?" A man called. "I am just getting off my shift at the hospital. I saw you were there tonight. Can I give you a lift home?"

"Oh. That's okay. I only live up there around the bend."

"I am going that way. You shouldn't be out here all alone, even in Heaven, there is darkness." The man pulled his car up beside her and opened the passenger door.

Guy! She thought. Get the hell out of here and leave me alone. His words were weird and she was ornery.

"It's not a big deal." But the open door was too inviting. Sliding into the seat she felt her body relax. "Take a left on Lakeshore and a right on Apache."

There was no more talking and Lisa was getting a little edgy at the stupidity of getting into this strange man's car. She sort of remembered him. He was wearing his own clothes now. He turned down Apache and she let out a breath. Quickly opening the door and jumping out as soon as he stopped she turned toward him.

"Thanks for the ride." Something weird about his shoes she thought looking down at his feet. The boots were shiny in the streetlight.

"You take good care now," he said put the car in drive and headed toward the dead end to turn around. She opened the door to the house. The car was moving back up to Lakeshore and she could clearly see it in the street light. A black Chevy Chevelle? No, it couldn't be. Her eyes were playing tricks on her. She double locked the door and went quickly to her room. With her parents sleepily heading upstairs she decided not to explain anything about the ride to them.

Jane looked up at her as she tucked her in.

"Lay in my bed until I fall asleep, please?" She asked

"Sure will," Lisa said as she snuggled up close to her sister. Too exhausted to worry, she fell fast asleep.

The milkman is already filling the milk box, Lisa thought, as she was awakened by the idling motor. She looked at the new digital clock. It's minute number just flipping with a noisy click. It was 3:45. Something's not right, she thought. It is an hour too early for the milkman.

She went to the darkened living room and peered out the window. Out near the mailbox sat a car. It was a model she didn't recognize. What do I do? Who do I call? Feeling vulnerable, she held her breath as the door opened and a figure got out of the passenger side. Clearly, this person was moving in the shadows and trying not to be seen. He inched his way up the driveway.

Acting quickly, Lisa grabbed a poker from the fireplace and a large frying pan that was hanging from the rack in the kitchen. She made her way along the unlit wall to the window beside the door. The person had made it up the drive. Why would someone sneak in the front door? She wondered poised to strike. The key was rustling in the door lock. There were a few seconds before she heard a loud "SHIT". The intruder had another lock to open. She was glad she thought to arm the door with both locks. But the deadbolt was unlocking now!

Puzzled, she watched the knob turn and was bringing the pan down to strike, when Billy yelled,

"Jesus! Hey! Watch out!"

"Billy?" Lisa cried. "I thought you were home. Whose car is that?"

"My friend's. Man, you could have killed me!"

"What are you doing out so late? I thought they released everybody."

"Look. The less you know, the better," He said dismissively. "Heaven has some interesting places open up when the sun goes down."

"Were you with Lamar, Billy?"

"Nope," he said, and took himself to the stairway. "Lock up, will ya?"

Lisa was thinking, as she locked the door, that her brother was such an ass.

Unable to sleep now, she pulled on an oversized Angels

sweatshirt and thought about sitting by the water. The slice of a crescent moon was just beginning to hang low in the sky. But her fear got the best of her. There were hidden fears lurking out there tonight. Opting for the overstuffed sectional, she looked out the window over the water and reflected on the past 24 hours.

Two things were bothering her. She wondered if the gun Lynn found was the actual murder weapon. Second, why did those shiny boots keep flashing alert messages in her head? An orderly wore black shiny boots to mop the floor at the hospital. Didn't orderlies and nurses wear those white shoes that didn't leave marks on tile? Although he had changed his clothes, his shoes stayed the same. Black. High shine. Side zipper.

"OH CRAP!" She said out loud. That man was Jed's father. He was guarding his son, I bet. How come he didn't hurt her on the ride home? What was the whole purpose of him picking her up? It was time to give Bobby a call.

Picking up the receiver, she looked at the clock. It was close to 5:00 AM. Maybe he wouldn't mind a call this early. She dialed the trim line phone in the guest room. It rang and rang. He wasn't there!

Hastily getting dressed, she left a quick note about heading to school early and almost collided with the milkman as he was filling the box. She took a bike out of the garage and didn't stop pedaling until she had made it to Lynn's. She didn't even know if Lynn would be home from the hospital, and planned to go from there to the police station, if that was the case.

Bobby Washington's car was in front of the house. Perfect,

she thought. She knocked lightly on the door. It took several minutes until a sleepy eyed Bobby opened the door.

"Girl!" He exclaimed. "Between you and your friend, I am never going to rest again."

"So, Lynn made it home last night?" Lisa asked.

"She did. She has had a good night. Not happy with me though. I had to wake her up every hour."

Bobby watched her look him up and down. He clarified, "She had a slight concussion. Good Lord, what do you take me for?"

"Bobby, what would you say if I told you Jed Adams' father was posing as an orderly at the hospital last night?"

Bobby looked at her. "You better come in," he said. "because if those cops up there didn't pick up on that, there will be hell to pay."

"What if I told you I walked home but accepted a ride from that orderly?" Lisa couldn't look him in the eye.

"I would say either you are pulling my leg or you're just plain stupid."

"Well, I am not pulling your leg," she said "And I only figured it out last night because he still had his black boots on."

"Good morning, honey bee." Zenobia was coming out of the kitchen with a steaming cup of tea. She was all dressed for work. "How did your evening go?"

Bobby shot a warning glance over to Lisa. She picked up what he was putting down. No upsetting Lynn's mom.

"It was okay," she said. "I am not sure my parents even knew I was gone."

"Oh honey. They knew." She smiled. "A precious child like you? They knew."

Lisa felt her eyes welling with tears. Oh, that she could feel that type of love.

"Do you mind if I check on Lynn?" She asked, marching into Lynn's bedroom without waiting for permission.

"Lisa! Girl! Where you been?" Lynn was sitting up in her bed. "Bobby said you probably got a ride home but you never stopped in."

"Lynn! I can't get you riled up," Lisa said. "But I do have some things to share." She told Lynn about her encounter in Jed's room and about the orderly with the boots and her ride home.

"Do you realize the danger you put yourself in?" Lynn asked, her eyes dark with disapproval. "We can't afford to get mixed up in this business."

"But we are Lynn!" Lisa said, "We are. Billy came home at 3:45 this morning. Was Lamar out that late?"

"I don't know, but Bobby says they are all done with their capers. They could have been charged," Lynn said. "Maybe he was with Lindsey."

"That's likely. I didn't recognize the car that brought him home though," Lisa said. "Either way, we have to find out about Jed's father. With him still out there and doing bold stuff like picking me up….Who's to say the next girl will be so lucky?"

Bobby walked in.

"Listen. I am running home to shower and put some fresh clothes on. Lisa, I am driving you to school."

Lisa looked at him long and hard. She didn't have any home-work done. Without a chance to catch up, she might be having to spend some time after school. But she knew Bobby was right for now. The cops needed to get with the program.

"I will come by practice and give you an update," he said. "Lynn, you only get out of that bed for food or bathroom. I will swing back around in a few hours."

Zenobia, Bobby, and Lisa all walked out together. The rest of the family was getting around, and bowls of cereal were clunking down on the counter. Lynn's siblings really weren't interested in what was happening with Lynn. Their lives had been spent with strangers coming in and out their whole lives. They took care of each other. Lynn was more like a junior version of their mother. They would rather not be noticed at all.

After the groups left the house quieted and Lynn lay back down. Her head was better but she was so exhausted. She closed her eyes and let sleep take her away.

Lisa

Lisa realized that the adventures of the past several months were wreaking havoc on her G.P.A. With the tennis team in a bye week she called her coach from the high school office.

"Coach," she said, as she watched all the office ladies tilt their heads ever so slightly in her direction. "I am just double checking on practice tonight. There is rain in the forecast."

"Lisa, you have missed a fair amount of practices this season." Coach Jan sounded a bit trite. "You know we have districts next week. Can't you wait to do your drama another week?"

"I was only going to see if I could go to after school tutoring for Geometry today. But it's cool. Our great tennis team sure needs to practice for districts." She hated being sarcastic but her focus had been split by a number of things and tennis wasn't one of them. She looked out the window and watched the black clouds roll in.

"Yeah. It's a perfect day to play." She hung up. That coach wasn't even a coach. She was a figurehead. They needed a warm body to coach this girls team now that Title Nine was in play. Last week, her coach had to look up how to play a tiebreaker in the MIDDLE of a match so they would do it correctly. It was embarrassing.

"Thank you, Mrs. Nelson," she said to the office helper. "I love a private phone call."

What was the matter with her? She was cranky and physically exhausted. She tapped on Charles Smith's shoulder. Charles was a bit of a geek, she knew, with his thick black glasses constantly needing a boost up his nose, but he was a master of Geometry. She needed help.

"Hey Charles? Might you have a minute at lunch to show me how to work those theorems? I am just not good at this at all."

Charles turned as if in shock. Lisa Palma wanted to have lunch with him?

"S-s-sure," he stammered. "I will meet you at the door of the cafeteria."

Smiling with thanks and relief, Lisa agreed and felt like she had one item checked off her list. With Jed at school, she wouldn't have even been able to say hello, let alone get help with math. She was so glad he was out of commission. Bobby and Lynn thought he might end up in Jackson at the juvenile facility in the middle of the state. They could ship him to Timbuktu for all she cared.

Bad memories started flashing forward. Pushing. Pushing. She couldn't hold them back. Her heart exploded from that little place she tucked all her hurts. She was bombarded with memories.

The doctor visit she made on her own the day after Jed had smacked her in the ear. The ear seemed to scream in pain. Dr. Morhan said she had a hole blown right through her ear drum. He asked how it happened. When she said she had been rough housing with her twin brothers, he calmly said that it did not happen that way. He asked some probing questions and Lisa realized that he thought that maybe her dad was beating her up. After several minutes of no suitable responses, Dr. Morhan said that if someone was hurting her she could tell him. She merely said she would but that wasn't the case here, so he had let it drop. Since then, she avoided the doctor altogether.

Just a few months ago Jed put his fist through the storm window of his house, during a beating. He lifted her up off the floor and positioned her to take a punch. She moved and his mother was on the bottom step when the entire window shattered. Screaming, Mrs. Adams tended to Jed's wounds, while Lisa ran over the shards of glass to freedom.

Jed told her once how silky the panties were of one of her tennis team mates he had been banging. He rationalized that if Lisa wasn't going to put out, he would rather leave her untouched down there. He had made mention of getting a higher price.

She felt the vomit rise to her mouth and ran into the nearest bathroom. There were six or seven girls smoking in the stall and she had to say excuse me before they budged. When she threw up, they all watched and exclaimed how nasty it was. She hated herself for showing them her vulnerability. Somehow she thought she'd done a good job hiding it.

"Heard your boyfriend is in the hospital," someone yelled. "That should have been you," the others were agreeing with the voice. They moved their circle a little closer.

"Back the hell up, people." It was Marcia Humphreys, a black cheerleader who took over Lisa's spot when she quit the team. "She didn't do anything to Lynn. Jed did. They aren't even together anymore. God, we are women! We should stick up for each other."

The circle began to slowly disperse, not without muttering.

"Thank you, Marcia. I feel like such a loser," Lisa said.

"Oh, girlfriend. You are no loser. They are all jealous of you. They love tearing a good person down. It just makes them feel better. You will bounce back from here and be on top again. It just takes time for people to forget. Keep your head up."

Lisa met Charles at the cafeteria. In less than 30 minutes he explained the finer points of theorems and how to get back on track in geometry. He offered to help her every lunch hour and she told him she would let him know. She didn't want to use the poor guy.

When the bell rang at 2:25 PM, she could not have been happier. She let a small amount of the baggage slide off her back today and let it go. Walking out on the freshly buffed linoleum in the entryway, she saw some club postings that she could sign up for on the bulletin board. She grabbed a few flyers. One was for a Girls Varsity Club and the other was for the Heaven High school Debate Team. Everyone loved Pat Kelly's mother, who was forming the new club varsity club, just for females in sports. She knew she could get into that one. The woman was so validating and nurturing. Many students called her "Mama" Kelly.

Walking out into the parking lot she noticed the pavement was full of puddles. It had rained most of the day and there would certainly be puddles on the courts. Another small victory. Coach Jan had put up a sign that said: *No Tennis today*. She whirled around quickly. Now to score a ride home.

But she was too late. It is amazing how a huge parking lot filled with cars can empty so fast! The line was just about done. She resigned herself to walk home. She thought she would hear from Lynn or Bobby but so far, no one had contacted her. She turned down Kalamazoo Street. She would go to see Lynn. She'd pick up her bike from weeks ago.

Wandering through the Zone on a gray, drizzly day made it look even more depressing. There were a few boys huddled under the overhang of the bathroom building at the park but they merely looked at her without turning their heads. In that look they assessed no threat. She knocked on Lynn's door.

Lynn

A month had passed since Lynn left the hospital. Life was slowly beginning to get back to normal. Today her doctors gave her the okay to resume all activities. She would head to school tomorrow. Bobby Washington hadn't been over so much since the team put Jed in the hospital. He was spending time with the State Police to try and put a case together. Jed Adams was of little help. He was spending his time in the infirmary at the City Jail in Kalamazoo. A larger facility, it was about 45 minutes from Heaven and housed some rough characters usually awaiting a trial or sentencing. Jed was in the same infirmary as the adults (18 and over). Any other teenager would be intimidated, but not Jed. He'd had a boat load of experience when his father was doing time. His dad would point out things to say and not say. He would instruct on how to keep your head down for the short hauls and how to lead the community if you were ever pinched for more than a year.

With William gone, Lynn felt freer to move about town. She saw Lisa coming up the driveway and opened the door. They hugged happily and Lynn wanted to know of anything happening at school. Lisa filled her in. Lamar and Billy left school together today, Lynn informed Lisa. She overheard they were getting into some sort of training group for teenagers wanting to get into law enforcement or something like that.

Lisa looked at Lynn.

They what? Her eyes said. They busted out laughing.

With the house to themselves, they ate chips and listened to a few of Lynn's new 45s. Lisa was fond of Motown but didn't have nearly the collection of songs Lynn did. The rainy May would soon give way to summer. Lisa was going to work at the drug store downtown and Lynn was going to babysit for some families in the neighborhood. They probably wouldn't see each other much.

Lynn felt them starting to drift apart. Life in this town had a way of doing that. Lisa was going on college visits already. Lynn thought about schools too but was still trying to decide. Her mother really needed her around the house lately and it was likely that Lynn would take some courses at the Community College, if she could spare the time.

Lisa sensed the feeling and said:

"You know, we will always be joined by this experience. Whatever we do in life."

"I know," Lynn sighed. "With Bobby all tied up, and you and me moving on, it's like a chapter from a book."

"Well, there are some things that still have to be resolved. First, they haven't found Jed's father. Second, Jed could be freed from the jail next week. If they don't find his dad he will be going to his mother's house."

"You forgot the third thing," a voice said as it came around the corner. The girls looked up shocked that there was someone in the house. "Gilbert has some unfinished business here."

The girls screamed. There stood Gilbert Morse. His time away had been spent in a dry out facility, and he appeared clear eyed and angry.

"Gilbert Morse! What are you doing in my house?" Lynn shouted, trying to be brave. She looked closer at Gilbert. He had gained weight. His clothes were clean. His short afro was neatly barbered.

"Seems my memory keeps coming back to me," he muttered "I remember things about you and YOU!" He was pointing a finger now. "I almost got killed with William that day. It was all so foggy for so long, but I can recollect the fact that you ladies were at the warehouse when all hell broke loose." He turned to Lisa and said,

"You think your daddy can save you and your metal tennis racket from all the lies you told? Or Lynn, what will your cop boyfriend think about the fact that his pretty little girlfriend has already laid with a man? Your world is about to get real, girls." He pulled out a gun. "Let's go. The car's waiting."

Lynn turned to her pillow. It looked like she was crying into it and hugging her teddy bear. Gilbert had the gun trained on Lisa, causing Lynn to stop crying and stand up. Lisa left her book bag right on the floor. If someone needed to look for Lynn, they would know they were together. She looked at the bed. The teddy bear's covering was unzipped. Shit! That meant Lynn was thinking ahead.

Lisa and Lynn got into the car. It was an older model Ford

Fairlane. Probably about a 1960 something. It was white but carried quite a bit of rust. The seats were uncomfortable and it was littered with greasy waxed paper and old Kalamazoo Gazettes. There were bits of food and pop bottles everywhere. Sticky remnants of doughnuts and crumbs were strewn across the floor. It looked like Gilbert had been living in this car!

Lisa saw the article on Jed Adams as it lay on the floor on the back seat of the Ford. A story had been written up in the Kalamazoo Gazette. She scanned it as Gilbert was pulling away. Jed was due to be arraigned on bond yesterday? She wasn't sure what that even meant. Gilbert put Lynn in the front seat with a hooded sweatshirt over her head.

Lisa asked Gilbert several times where they were heading, as she saw the city fade away to become acres and acres of uncleared land. This seemed like the route up to the cabin.

As they turned a corner she looked behind her. It seemed like the whole area was deserted. Off to the left, she saw an old fruit stand. There was a car there. It wasn't one she recognized but if she could get away, she would make that be her focal point.

Lisa and Lynn

The road was more rutted than she remembered. There had been a lot of rain making these dirt roads nearly impassable. The rear tire got mired down in the mud and Gilbert couldn't go any further.

"This is fine," he muttered. "You got feet, you can walk."

Inside the cabin glowed with light from a lantern. Illuminated in the window were Jed and his father. They were looking over a map and looked up when they heard the car. Benny came out first, his gun held along the side of his leg. It was a small pistol and didn't look as dangerous as the man himself. Jed followed closely. He carried no weapon.

Gilbert smiled and said: "Told you I can be trusted, Benny. These two were just waiting to be picked up. Just like two hookers walking the street."

"Shut up!" Jed said, and he hauled off and slapped Gilbert so hard he fell, dropping his gun as he sprawled, landing with a plop in a mud filled rut. "That's where you belong, you stupid pig."

"What the hell, man?" Gilbert sputtered, his face covered in mud. "I was just making a joke."

"Jed. Lay off, right now, okay?" Benny was soothing Jed. "We know the girl did you wrong, but you can't let the fact that you cared for her cloud your judgment. That will wear off soon enough. Let's go inside."

They were still a ways from the cabin. The girls stumbled through the murky underbrush and mud. Lisa fell, landing on her hands and knees precariously close to Gilbert's gun. She reached out and slid it into the sleeve of her coat as she got back to her feet. She hoped it would be intimidating enough so she wouldn't need to shoot. She would have to act quickly when they were all inside.

'Hurry up and get the lead out. Gilbert, once you get out of that shit, go and check the road. We don't want a tail when we leave."

Gilbert looked put out. He wanted to be a vital part of the operation. This guy was ordering him around as if he didn't owe him something for all the bullets he put into his chest the day William died. He felt rejected again. He muttered as he shook mud from his leg and headed back toward the old two lane highway.

The girls looked at each other. We are back in the same damn place.

It was now or never, Lisa thought. She let the gun drop into her hand and slowly raised it to Jed's head.

"If you want your son alive, Benny, you better give Lynn your gun." She spoke loud and slow.

Jed had a look of utter disbelief as he heard his father chuckle.

"Go ahead and off him little girl," he said "He has become

more of a headache than Gilbert! I run a tidy operation and this kid of mine…"

BAM! Before he could finish, Lisa switched, as if in a tennis game, from forehand to backhand and pulled the trigger. It caught Benny Forter just above the ear. He looked hateful at first, quickly changing to frightened, and finally slumped down with blood leaking out of his head. His gun fell loose but Lynn didn't grab it. She produced one of her own.

Jed sprang into action. He was stunned that this girl whom he loved, in his sick way, had just shot his father. The words his father just said about his worth still made his heart hurt. He thought they were getting closer every day. This was the longest he had been together with his dad since grade school and he was feeling some sort of approval or connection. Sweeping his arm around Lisa's neck, he looked at Lynn.

"Let's see just how good a shot you are, Lynn." Jed yanked harder and Lisa's head flew back, her body lifted off the floor. She was finding it harder to breathe.

"Shoot him, Lynn. Shoot the gun!" Lisa rasped out.

Lynn was thinking back to her basketball days at the park. They were playing another park for the championship. Her brother was in the crowd yelling, "come on Lynn, pop it." She steadied herself and made the shot. The ball went in. She put herself back there now. Her friend was no longer gasping for air. She sagged in Jed's arm at the same time that Lynn squeezed the trigger.

At first, nothing seemed to happen. Lynn fired again. This time Lisa fell onto the ground and Jed fell in the opposite direction with two clean holes beginning to turn his sweater pink. There was a foam building up as if in an egg cream soda. She must have hit him in the lung. His eyes were dimming. Lisa began coughing on the floor of the cabin. Lynn looked at her, stricken.

"Are you all right?" Lynn screamed.

But Lisa seemed not to hear her. Standing up, she went over to the makeshift cot, still there from when Jed held Lynn captive. She removed the pillow and gently laid it on Jed's face.

"I hope you find peace." She said and pushed down gently with both hands. She was met with little resistance and after a few minutes, Lynn lifted her hands up off the pillow. She replaced the pillow on the bed and grabbed Lisa by the hand, saying,

"There is still Gilbert."

They walked out the door and could see Gilbert coming up the road with three others.

"Get back!" Lynn whispered, pushing Lisa well back into the brush. They would need to stay hidden, as any movement would give their whereabouts away. Lisa sat down putting a few overgrown branches over them.

Watching the group grow larger and more distinct, the girls realized that it was Gilbert, yes, but the three others began to sharpen until Lynn gasped, catching her breath deep in her throat.

"Lisa! It's Bobby Washington and he's got Billy and Lamar with him."

"Don't move yet," Lisa whispered. "We don't know if Gilbert has any more weapons."

"He's holding a handgun," Lynn said. "But then so are Bobby and our brothers."

Lisa got up on her hands and knees. She watched the men tentatively step up on the porch while the brothers stood to either side of the cabin.

"Well, I'll be damned," Bobby exclaimed and then whistled. "Either Lisa and Lynn have put these men away or they have killed each other."

The boys scrambled inside. Gilbert pointed to the gun near Jed's body. "That's my gun. I dropped it after that little prick cold cocked me in the face."

"Don't touch anything. Billy, Lamar, go get the car. I need to radio this in. Gilbert and I will look for the girls."

Lynn stood then. She didn't realize that her face was spattered with the blood from Jed's lung wound. It looked as if someone had taken a paintbrush and shook it at her. Lisa had leaves and detritus from the brush and ground all over her head, but they were pretty much unscathed as they stepped out of their hiding place.

"Bobby!" Lynn yelled. "We're over here."

Bobby Washington spun around on one foot and took a giant step with the other. He didn't know how, but these girls had taken down a criminal he had been chasing for over two years. A car was coming up the road too quickly for the potholes and muddy ruts. It bounced in the air a few times but could not get any closer than Gilbert's car, still immobilized with mud up over the rims. The boys jumped out quickly. They went to their sisters and exchanged awkward hugs. All the stake out training they had been doing with the members of the State Police paid off. They were able to see where Benny and Jed were hiding out, well before Gilbert arrived. Although, they couldn't have known how the situation would unfold.

When the police arrived, they got a statement from Lynn and Lisa. What was shocking was that they didn't put Gilbert in handcuffs.

"Bobby?" Lynn asked. "Why is Gilbert Morse not in handcuffs?"

"Lynn, Gilbert agreed to work with us on exposing the trafficking ring for a reduction to his sentence. Looks like he will just be charged with a misdemeanor and credit for time served," Bobby said.

"So that's it?" Lynn said. "He will walk free?"

"Lynn, is there something you need to tell me?" Bobby searched from her face to Lisa's.

Lisa shook her head slowly at Lynn to indicate no and Lynn followed it up with:

"I don't ever want to see him again."

Bobby laughed and said, "I am pretty sure he won't be bothering you two any longer. Your brothers have made it clear to him that he is not wanted, liked, or respected. Lamar says he was nothing but a mooch to your family."

Lynn was quiet. She could have called Gilbert out right then for raping her. But she didn't want it to get out in public. She was ashamed and embarrassed.

Lisa said, "Bobby, can we go? We have a lot to talk about."

Bobby Washington held up one finger.

"After I finish your statements, you are to go straight home."

He called over to Lamar and Billy.

"These boys will give you a lift," he said. "I will let you know what the D.A. says when the case is unraveled."

"Not sure what that means," Lisa said.

"Well, there are two men dead here. The D.A. will decide whether or not the people will press charges."

"Against who?" Lisa asked. "Us?"

"It's just a formality," Bobby said. "They may need further statements, and don't leave town."

Lisa

The group was quiet all the way back into town. The brothers were acting like they were the cats that ate the canaries. Lisa was sitting in the back seat anxiously wondering if they should get lawyers while Lynn, who'd had more excitement than she had had in over a month, settled back and closed her eyes.

Oh, friend, Lisa thought, I sure hope we can close the door to all this.

Riding out the next few days was rough. Every time the phone rang, Lisa was sure it would be the cops. Her father told her she had done the right thing, but took her down to St. Leonards to make a complete confession so God would "get" all the details.

Looking at Father Hambring through the grate of the confessional, Lisa gave as little of the story as she could. Hungry for information, he was asking question after question wanting details. When he realized that he was not going to receive anything further other than monosyllabic responses, he reluctantly absolved her with a penance that included 12 Our Fathers, six Hail Mary's, and one Apostle's Creed.

Kneeling at the communion railing in the darkened church,

Lisa unceremoniously said her prayers of absolution. When she was finished she continued to kneel. Feeling her eyes filling up with tears, she wept in hard, racking sobs. Even though she denied it to everyone, even though he beat her dozens of times, even though she was publicly humiliated, she hated herself for what had happened. This love in her heart for Jed was still there. Why? She had been driven to kill another living person. She would regret that for the rest of her life.

Her eyes were red and puffy as she began the short mile walk toward home. She decided to walk home via the beach so she could collect herself out of the public eye. She and Lynn had become overnight celebrities it seemed. The Kalamazoo Gazette, Herald Palladium, and Heaven's Daily Tribune all sent reporters around. Her statement was given by Neal Harold, the family's attorney.

"Please respect the privacy of the families involved in the matter. This is an ongoing police investigation."

Lynn called Lisa almost every day, but it seemed as if this episode caused each to recede back into their places of comfort. They rarely met in person. Summer arrived, and with that came jobs and commitments and parties outside of school.

By mid-July, the case of Benny Forter and his son Jed had been completed. There were no more charges posted. Gilbert Morse was sent to Camp Lehman in Grayling. His sentence was three to five years.

Lisa read less and less about this encounter and was trying to stay in tune with the war ending in Vietnam, her college choices, and anything that would help her erase the memory of the past few years. If it bubbled up, she quickly got busy doing something to help her forget. She felt Lynn knew she was avoiding her but she felt she needed time away to heal.

Lynn

The summer was going too fast. Senior picture forms were coming in the mail. This sure was going to be a fun year. Lynn spent the majority of her time this summer babysitting for the kids in the neighborhood; mostly for the mothers from her church. They knew she had a kind heart and always organized fun activities for the kids.

Lynn brought the mail inside and looked at the flyer. Senior pictures at the local photography studio were showcased in their windows. Sometimes whole family portraits were placed there too. Lynn recognized Lisa's family in the window. It was taken outdoors in the garden. Her parents were in back, the older kids were flanking the sides and the twins held the dog in the center. They all had on pretty hip clothes. Lynn saw that Lisa got her hair cut. Her little sister Jane must have just kicked into puberty. Since her brother and Lamar graduated, it seemed they both had intentions to marry their high school sweethearts.

Life keeps moving, Lynn thought. If you don't make the effort to be a friend, then that connection runs through your fingers like water. She decided she'd have to give Lisa a call.

Things with Bobby Washington had really cooled down. He

rarely came over to check on them anymore. She heard the scuttlebutt that he was dating someone from Grand Rapids he met during police training of some sort. Bad timing, she thought.

There were a million handsome guys at the park on the weekends. She enjoyed the dance parties in the street near Moon Park. The Williams girls were bomb dancers. One of them, Denice, was a Soul Train dancer and would come home to teach the newest line dances to the neighborhood girls. Lined up behind her, the girls would do the Funky Chicken as Rufus Thomas' voice blasted out of Denice's upstairs window on the hifi speaker. Next, the crowds of kids would mix it up doing the "Bump". It was a silly easy dance and Lynn would go from person to person as strains of the Commodores' Brick House wafted over the crowd. These were happy teenage memories.

Lynn and Lisa

After spending the summer apart, Lynn and Lisa entered high school together as seniors. They went to lunch together and figured out schedules that would put them together at least three times a day, plus lunch.

"You know, Lynn," Lisa said one day while downing one of Mrs. Holland's delicious pizza burgers, "if you come to Kalamazoo next year we could be roommates."

"Or you could stick around here and we could run this town," Lynn grinned. "Whatever happens, I love you like a sister and I know where I can go when I need a friend."

Lisa had tears in her eyes.

"I love you back, then."

"Let's write a book together someday," Lynn said.

"I like that idea."

THE END

From student to teacher, thank you Jeremy Brown.

Made in the USA
Monee, IL
31 January 2021